The Guide To Successful
Jewish Homemaking

It's
About
Time...

It's About

Tamar
Books

Time...

The Guide To Successful Jewish Homemaking

NECHAMA BERG
CHAYA LEVINE

FIRST EDITION
First Impression . . . October 1992

Distributed by
MESORAH PUBLICATIONS, Ltd.
4401 Second Avenue
Brooklyn, New York 11232
(718) 921-9000

Distributed in Israel by
MESORAH MAFITZIM / J. GROSSMAN
Rechov Harav Uziel 117
Jerusalem, Israel

Distributed in Australia & New Zealand by
GOLD'S BOOK & GIFT CO.
36 William Street
Balaclava 3183, Vic., Australia

Distributed in Europe by
J. LEHMANN HEBREW BOOKSELLERS
20 Cambridge Terrace
Gateshead, Tyne and Wear
England NE8 1RP

Distributed in South Africa by
KOLLEL BOOKSHOP
22 Muller Street
Yeoville 2198
Johannesburg, South Africa

IT'S ABOUT TIME
© *Copyright 1992, by* TAMAR BOOKS

ISBN:
0-89906-111-7 (hard cover)
0-89906-112-5 (paperback)

Typography by CompuScribe at ArtScroll Studios, Ltd.
4401 Second Avenue / Brooklyn, N.Y. 11232 / (718) 921-9000

Printed in the United States of America by Noble Book Press Corp.
Bound by Sefercraft, Quality Bookbinders, Ltd. Brooklyn, N.Y.

In Memory

of

Our Mothers

חנה בת אליהו ע״ה

צפורה בת יוסף אהרן ע״ה

ᴥ§ *Table of Contents*

Section I:
The Five Step Management System

↪§ *Acknowledgments*

My acknowledgements must start with my gratitude to Hashem who granted me abilities and guided me with His Divine *hashgachah* into the right situations to develop them.

I would like to thank everyone in my family for everything you are and for everything you have done for me. In this short space, words cannot express all that I feel. A special thanks to my naturally organized sister who happily shared a room with me for so long. To my sister-in-law Brenda Markovitz, who patiently listened to all my ideas and read through every questionable piece, her input was invaluable. To all my teachers, rebbetzins, and friends, who have so wisely advised me over the years and given of their precious time; to my clients from whom I've learned so much.

To ArtScroll, Jerusalem and the New York staff who made this book a reality. To Debbie Ismailoff who edited our work on Erev Pesach with a smile.

I am grateful to my wonderful husband for patiently waiting for supper and never complaining. And to my children who sometimes stayed indoors on a nice day so that mommy could finish writing. May Hashem grant us the *zechus* and strength to continue doing *mitzvos*.

Chaya Levine
Jerusalem

My deepest appreciation to:

My aunt and uncle, Rabbi Chaim Baruch and Esther Gelernter, who love me like their own child. My cousins, Eva Gelernter and Rosette Narkunski, whose homes were always open to me. My mother-in-law,

Dr. Natalie Berg, for her constant encouragement and support. My sisters-in-law, Joanna Finkelstein and Jenny Berg, for their warm friendship.

Rabbi Pinchos Wasserman and his wife Rivky, for more than I can write in this short space.

Mr. and Mrs. Arthur and Tamar Gordon, for all of the wonderful Shabbosim and Yomim Tovim we spent with them.

Dr. Harriet Feldman, who shared her time and knowledge during the initial stages of this project.

All of my friends, whose inspiration and advice contributed to this book.

ArtScroll Publishers, with a special thanks to Mr. Shmuel Blitz for his invaluable assistance.

To my dear husband, Yonason, and my children, Mindy, Eliyahu, Yosef Aaron, Chana Bluma, and Bracha Yehudis. May Hashem grant us the privilege of raising our children to be *tzaddikim* and *yirei shomayim*.

With gratitude to Hashem for making it all possible.

Nechama Berg
Jerusalem

This book was written for and dedicated to
you, the *aishes chayil*
who is striving to build a *bayis ne'eman b'Yisrael*.

You may come from a home where your mother was the consummate Jewish woman, spending hours cooking, cleaning and doting over you, or from a home where your mother worked, whipping up dinner in fifteen minutes. You may be an only child or one of twelve. You may be from the heart of Boro Park or the suburbs of Chicago. You may have gotten married at eighteen or thirty-eight. You may possess a strong religious background or have discovered you were Jewish last week.

Maybe you are the newlywed who doesn't understand how women can sit around discussing recipes and secrets of cleaning all day long. Maybe you are the perfect mother and working woman who succeeds at both jobs as long as you have a cleaning lady.

Every one of us has a special background and personality. Each one of us has a similar yet distinct set of values and goals. Each one of us has her own unique tests, trials, husband and children.

This book, *be'ezras Hashem,* will help you create your own personalized home management system. You may recognize yourself in some of these vignettes, and you may find some chapters in this book more applicable to you than others. With *tefillah* and *siyatta dishemaya* may we all succeed in creating our own *bayis ne'eman b'Yisrael.*

✑ Introduction

During one of our home management lectures a woman in the audience stood up to ask a question. "Your life is different from mine," she said. "You don't have the same number of children that I do. Your home is not the same size as mine. How, then, can your advice actually help me in my situation?"

When she was through, a murmur was heard through the audience. We overheard someone else sitting in the front row voicing a similar complaint. I turned to my questioner and asked her, "When you become sick, do you go to the doctor?"

"Of course I do," she answered.

"Well," I continued, "has your doctor come down with every illness described in the medical books?"

"Of course not," she answered.

"If that is the case then why do you seek his advice? He might not have suffered from the same illness that you have."

"He doesn't have to come down with my illness to know how to treat me," she stammered. "He studied in medical school and has years of experience treating patients."

"Ah," I said "You've answered your own question. A person doesn't have to have the same problem in order to help others — knowledge and experience is enough." Satisfied, she sat down to listen to our lecture.

Who are we? You might imagine us to be *bubbies* with a few generations of *nachas* in front of us and sixty years of experience behind us. Or you might imagine us to be super-*balabustas* with floors and tiles that sparkle twenty-four hours a day, gourmet food at every meal and closets that could double as display cases.

Actually you may be surprised to discover that we are neither of the above. We are two married women who joined together to start a business called Creative Options. Our goal was to counsel women who wanted information on how to start a home business.

When we opened our doors to religious women throughout Israel, we received visits from women living in Israel temporarily, who wanted information and advice before returning to their homes in the United States, England, and South Africa. We met many different types of women from all over the globe. During our counseling sessions, many women admitted to us that they were having difficulty managing their homes and children. They didn't know how to find the time to manage a home business also.

Although my partner and I were able to offer some time-saving tips to our clients, we realized that in order to address their concerns properly, we would have to go out and do systematic research on home management. We consulted with rebbetzins, psychologists, time-management lecturers, professional cleaning women and organized women. We spoke to mothers of twelve children, *bubbies* who still had children at home, women who raised all-boy families, working women, and women who made homemaking their full-time professions. Then we delved into books. We read books (that are not available at your local bookstore) written by university professors describing studies conducted on thousands of American women and the skills needed to manage household chores. We read popular books on time management, household organization, household tips, efficient cooking methods, interior decoration, space-saving techniques and storage suggestions. Once we started we couldn't stop. We had discovered the fascinating science of housekeeping.

It became clear to us that there wasn't one system for efficiency in the home. Different systems were successful for different women. And more importantly, we learned that each woman's system had to be adaptable to changes in her life, such as the birth of a child, the move to a new house or the beginning of a new job.

We set down our impressions on paper and we had a unique new counseling service to offer our clients. Soon we were lecturing to women's organizations. At the end of the lectures women would make appointments to meet with us for individual consultations. Thus began a new offshoot of our business in which we made private home visits to assess each woman's unique situation. After the consultations were over our clients usually requested a book to keep them motivated and on track. It was a good idea. This is the result.

In this book we would like to share our knowledge and experience with you. We'll begin by saying that getting organized requires five very important steps. These steps do not have to be done in the sequence listed here (they can be done in order of priority), but all the steps must be covered to achieve total organization.

Here is the five step system:

Step 1 — Davening for Help
Step 2 — Time for Everything
Step 3 — Systematic Cleaning
Step 4 — Household Organization
Step 5 — Meal Management

Step 1 is the most important of the five. Recognize that *siyatta dishemaya*, help from above, is the only route to success. So *daven* first, before you begin to work. It will put you on the right track, and, in the end, everything will unfold as it should — *gam zu le'tovah*, this too is for the best.

Step 2 is about time. Sometimes the focus of our lives becomes blurred. We become overwhelmed by laundry, dishes and cleaning, but we all know these chores don't constitute our ultimate purpose. It isn't the physical surroundings, but the people in our lives and the spiritual activities — Torah and *mitzvos* — that matter most. Therefore, we must find a way to streamline our household routine and spend our precious time on those things which are most important to us.

Step 3 is the cleaning system. It will clarify your cleaning needs by helping you create priorities for your household tasks. Then you will design a workable schedule to keep your house running smoothly.

Step 4 is the guide to spacial organization. It will help you find a place for all of your possessions and assist you in evaluating your present storage needs.

Step 5 provides the key to setting up a meal management system. Read about the four ingredients necessary for meal organization and decide for yourself which food preparation system will work best for you.

Then read on and enjoy the chapters about Shabbos and Yom Tov, effectively delegating jobs to children, advice for mothers of large families, to name a few. After you have finished, give this book to your husband because we[1] prepared a chapter especially for him.

A Word about Words

A few weeks ago a reporter for a prominent parent's magazine called and asked to interview me. She had heard about my business through a friend of hers and was impressed. One of the first things she wanted to know was whether I recommended "routines" to my clients. "Routines? Absolutely not," I replied. "I don't teach routines. I create personalized schedules and cleaning systems." How do I manage my own schedule? "I set aside times and assign jobs to specific days." Like a routine? "No, a schedule," I repeated. This verbal exchange went on for another ten minutes until I realized that the word *routine* held negative connotations for me. My life was busy, organized and enjoyable, certainly not a dull routine. But to the reporter, the word *schedule* was negative; she preferred *routine*. Why?

"Routine is lively and rythmic," she responded, "like a dance routine or comedy routine."

Although we were both talking about the same idea, we needed the right word to make it work. Take the time now to discover whether words commonly associated with maintenance or household organization possess negative associations in your mind. If they do, then mentally substitute other words in their place. Here is a list: method, procedure, process, practice, manner, formula, system, plan and structure.

To illustrate the importance of words with another example, some women work efficiently at the office but don't do as well at home. In part, this is because at work everything is well-defined, whereas home maintenance can be more flexible and therefore more prone to mismanagement. When counseling clients with this problem, I recommended creating a schedule for running their homes, and many of them balked. However, when I suggested creating a *system* or *operation* they accepted the idea and were successful at getting it to work for them. In addition, many women told me that their improved skills at home reflected in their work performance. So choose your words carefully.

---

1. Although this book is the result of our combined efforts, from this point onward we will refer to ourselves as "I" for purposes of simplicity and clarity.

SECTION I:

THE FIVE STEP MANAGEMENT SYSTEM

Step One
Daven for Help

As women, we have all experienced "those days." Those days when even the no-fail recipe flopped. When that favorite coffee cup just slipped out of our hands. When we planned to run a dozen errands and the car broke down. When, armed to the teeth with cleaning equipment and ready for a final assault on the house, the teacher called — 6-year-old Esty fell and needs stitches. Those days when the baby wouldn't take a nap and the kids seemed more wild than usual. It's not that we didn't plan. We even woke up on time. But nothing seemed to go our way.

I would love to promise that if you put all of our home management principles into practice, you will never have another one of "those days." But I'd be leaving out an integral part of the picture if I didn't mention an additional factor. No section on household organization or time management for religious women could be complete without a reminder that there is a Higher Authority in control. We need His assistance to get the job done. Without it, all of our efforts are in vain. We can plan schedules, write lists, make charts, draw diagrams and work twelve hours straight, but we can't succeed without Hashem's help.

To give an example, I was asked to lecture on time management to a group of women in a Jerusalem suburb. The class was called for 8:30 and I wanted to demonstrate that organization leads to punctuality. By 7:30 that evening I was dressed and ready. At 7:50 I had already called for a cab. I waited and waited and waited. Then I called the company to remind them that I was still waiting. Finally the taxi arrived — with three other passengers. "Surely you won't mind if I drop them off first and then take you to your destination?" the taxi driver "asked" me. Annoyed, I entered the cab, and as the minutes ticked by, I scrutinized every move of the past hour: I asked myself, "Should I have called the taxi earlier? Should I have dialed another company when the first one didn't arrive?" But I could only conclude that I had made the normal effort and what happened was simply beyond my control. For some reason I was meant to be late! When I arrived, red-faced, to teach the time-management class, I spoke with great emotion on the vital element of *siyatta dishemaya*, help from Above, in determining our success.

Recognizing that the outcome of our efforts is not totally within our control will alter our outlook. Rather than berate ourselves when plans don't work out as anticipated, we can accept whatever happens as the will of Hashem. We can say *gam zu le'tovah*, this too is for the best, aware of the value of a *nissayon*, trial, and a *kapparah*, atonement. We can praise ourselves for the effort we made and for cultivating the attitude of *gam zu le'tovah*. And we can *daven* for *siyatta dishemaya*, recognizing that it is only with Hashem's help that our hard work will bear fruit.

In addition, *davening* can help prevent despair when the situation seems too difficult to handle. A friend of mine with many small children told me her secret to coping so well. She constantly reminded herself that if Hashem put her in this situation, then she was strong enough to handle it. As soon as she'd feel her strength ebb she would *daven* to Him for the ability to continue. She believes this is the reason women survive during the week before Pesach. Where else could they get such stamina?

I have also made use of this uplifting concept when my own spirits were down. Once, it was a cold Thursday evening and the electrician came to fix a light switch. I was behind in my Shabbos preparations and standing knee-deep in dishes, bowls and half-completed recipes. As I was pouring the flour onto the rolling board the electrician broke the news. The switch wasn't working because of a major electrical problem necessitating the immediate removal of my Pesach cabinet, which was located smack in the middle of my kitchen. The timing couldn't have been worse. My knees became weak and my stomach started churning. How was I going to manage? So I stopped what I was doing and uttered a heartfelt prayer that Hashem give me the mental and physical energy to finish all of my preparations on time. The electrician stayed until 2:00 A.M. and to my amazement I was able to complete my work in a patient and calm manner.

STEP ONE AT A GLANCE

1. Recognize that everything is not in our control. Therefore, pray for Hashem's help.
2. If, after exerting our best efforts, things do not work out as planned, realize that everything Hashem does is for our benefit.

Step Two
Time for Everything

Early morning. Rochel is groggily aware of little fingers poking at her face, tickling her toes and voices whispering, "Sh, you're not allowed to wake up Imma." In the carriage next to her bed lies the baby, whose crying has reached a crescendo despite his brother's valiant attempts to comfort him. Resigning herself to the inevitable, Rochel sits up in bed and is greeted by two pairs of large, brown eyes staring intently into her face. "You awake, Imma?" Moshe asks. "Oh, Imma's awake," they shout in unison, jumping up and down on the bed. Rochel feels as though she were rocking in a storm-tossed boat. She wonders how and why she'd booked this passage.

Glancing at the clock, she realizes there is only half an hour to dress two boys, decide what to put in their lunch boxes and make sure they get to the corner in time for the school bus. Mismatched socks, torn pants, shirts with buttons missing and underwear with no elastic seem to be all that is available. Tracking down a *kippah* is like searching for a UFO. "Here, put on the one mommy used as a potholder last night," Yossi advises his brother.

After rummaging through the bread bags which contain only the ends of the bread, she grabs a frozen roll used every Shabbos as the *lechem mishneh* spare and throws it into a bag. Then she spots one slice of bread and spreads some jelly on it. "Not jelly! I want, cheese, cheese, cheese!" yells Yossi.

"Did you brush your teeth?" she asks as she scrapes the jelly off the previous slice of bread. "Where are your shoes?" she shouts frantically as she spreads honey on two rice cakes. She shoves the "breakfast" into their hands and scoots them out the door.

The telephone is ringing. Rochel dashes to answer it but picks it up too late. The line goes dead.

Devorah is chanting, "I'm hungry, I want a rice cake and honey, rice cake and honey." As Rochel prepares it, the phone rings again. Thinking that the call may be about a change in the school bus schedule, she answers it.

"Hi, Rochel, it's Dad," the voice on the other end of the line says. "Why didn't you pick up the phone earlier?" Listening to her baby shrieking in the background, Rochel is tempted to tell her father-in-law to call back later. "Is Avraham there?" he continues.

"No," she answers, distracted, "he's not back from shul yet."

Suddenly Devorah begins to shout, "*Zeidy, Zeidy,* I want to talk to him." She grabs the phone from her mother and says, "Hello, *Zeidy.* When are you coming to take me to the zoo?" Just then Avraham walks in and Devorah hands him the phone.

Why can't I get my act together? Rochel criticizes herself. Leaving the rice cake for Devorah, she hurries off to pick up the baby. Another day has begun.

❧ ❧ ❧

The rest of Rochel's day did not proceed much more smoothly, nor did the rest of her week. She felt that her life resembled a roller coaster ride; she was simply unable to control the direction in which she was headed.

There is a solution to Rachel's problem. It is part of the second step to total organization which is to master time management. The term time management is often used but seldom understood. What do you think of when you hear the words *time management*? Do you envision someone running robot-like in a film being played on too fast a speed? Or do you think of a woman who can account for every minute of her day, devoid of spontaneity and imagination? You're probably nodding your head in agreement, yet, the opposite is true. Proper time management enables you to achieve what is really important, training you to differentiate between the important and the immediate. (What is immediate is not always important.) It prevents you from overloading your day.

Rochel, like many others, has little time to herself. She feels pulled in all directions, her husband, children, neighborhood organizations, and *chesed* activities all demanding her time and attention. What should she do first? Second? Feeling over-whelmed, she decides that a lesson on time management is her top priority and she calls me for an appointment. I advise her that for our first meeting she is to bring a week-at-a-glance appoint-ment calendar, and if she doesn't own one, she should buy one.

≈§ Establishing Priorities

When Rochel arrived for our meeting, the first thing I asked her to do was to write down her current responsibilities and activities. The list included: housework, *gemach,* children's homework, shopping, *shiurim,* exercise class, organizing the photo album. Upon completing it she was visibly shaken. This was really "mission impossible," she concluded. I reassured her that this list was the first step towards success. Then I advised her to decide which activities were important to her, which were immediate and necessary, and which should be delegated to someone else or eliminated altogether.

I elaborated. "Important activities are those which add inspiration, creativity, and spice to your life. They are not the activities you can or will spend all your time on, but they should be included in your schedule at least once a week. Included in this category might be attending *shiurim,* studying informally, learning a new skill, taking a correspondence course, swimming, or being involved in any activity which you look forward to. Necessary activities are things which must be done in order for you and your home to function. These include cleaning, cooking, mending — the time consuming elements of our days."

"But I have written down so much," she lamented. "Where do I begin?"

"You haven't yet divided the list according to priorities," I explained. "Let's do it now. Draw a star (*) next to important activities, a plus sign (+) next to necessary activities, and cross out any jobs to be delegated, writing down the name of the person to whom it will be delegated.

"Think carefully. If you know that a certain project is presently impossible or unrealistic, cross it off the list. When in doubt, put a question mark (?) next to the item. For example, suppose you've always wanted to take a gourmet cooking course, but you don't know of any available. As you review your list of projects, you realize that cooking classes don't seem as important as your other projects, yet you still have the desire to attend such a course. You don't have to decide immediately. Put a question mark next to 'cooking course' and if a class doesn't materialize then cross it off your list. Or, if you go home and your friend calls to let you know that a renowned *balabusta* is giving a four-week course two blocks from your house, you might convert the question mark to a star."

Rochel picked up her pen and began marking each item on her list. When she finished I elaborated. "Establishing priorities enables you to incorporate all of your activities into a workable schedule."

Rochel looked at me inquisitively. "Will I really be able to do all that I want to do?" she asked.

I assured her that she could if she scheduled each task in the appropriate time slot. "A weekly schedule including at least one time slot for a Torah *shiur*, sewing class, exercise class or similar activity will help you to break the cycle of always letting the important take a back seat to the 'immediate.' It is a system that is simple to maintain. All that you need are a week-at-a-glance appointment book and a master list of projects, ideas and tasks that you *must* do and those that you *want* to do."

❧ Matching the Time to the Task

I went on to explain the system in greater detail. "At the beginning of the week, schedule all appointments and chores that can be attended to only at specific times. Next, schedule 'important,' then 'necessary' tasks. When you plan, be sure to take into account the 'Internal Time-Task Match.' "

"What?" Rochel asked, bewildered.

"Let me explain," I said. "Certain times in the day are more suited to certain tasks. By keeping in mind that specific activities require physical energy, others demand mental clarity, and some require neither, you can adjust your schedule accordingly. Physically demanding tasks should be synchronized with times when your energy level is at its peak; mentally demanding tasks should be synchronized with those times when you are most alert. Plan activities that require neither physical nor mental energy for those periods when you are low on both."

Rochel started to write. Looking up from her notebook, she exclaimed, "I get it! Now let me give you some examples." Her enthusiasm was contagious. I sat forward to listen. "When I must vacuum the carpets before Shabbos I should do it when I'm feeling energetic. If I don't do it then, it will take twice as long and I won't do it well. To balance my checkbook accurately I should do it when I can think clearly; if I don't, mistakes are sure to creep in. When I'm tired I should sew, because I can just sit and it doesn't take a lot of physical energy. When my mental energy is spent I can wash the dishes and let my mind wander." Rochel smiled, realizing how the Time-Task Match would make planning easier.

"Let's devise a graph to come up with a picture of your energy levels," I suggested. In a few moments I handed her a sheet of paper. It looked something like this:

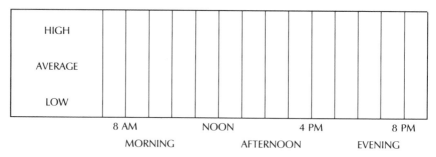

At this point, I told her to make a line reflecting her energy level during the day. Rochel's chart looked like this:

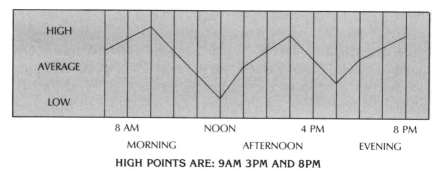

HIGH POINTS ARE: 9AM 3PM AND 8PM

"You call this the 'Internal Time-Task Match.' Does that mean that there is an '*External* Time-Task Match'?" she asked.

"You guessed it!" I answered. "If you didn't take external circumstances into consideration your solutions would be impractical. You must take the whole picture into account. You might have the physical energy to clean and organize the pantry when your children are home, but they might have other plans. You might have a long stretch of quiet in the morning to work on a correspondence course, but you might lack the mental alertness to concentrate at that time.

"Fortunately, however, there usually is more than one period in the day when we are either very high or very low on the graph." I leaned over to look at her graph with her. "For example, you have high energy levels at 9 A.M., 3 P.M. and 8 P.M. You don't have to clean out the pantry when the kids are home at 3 P.M. — you can do it at 9 A.M. or 8 P.M. Or, you can eliminate the external problem in this case and hire a baby sitter to take out the children, or ask a neighbor if they can play at her house."

ᴥ§ Scheduling Magic

"Now, let's get down to business," I said. "Take out your week-at-a-glance appointment book. First, schedule any current responsibilities (such as carpool or a part-time teaching position) that occur at specific times during the week. Next, schedule time for important activities. Then, schedule housework: cooking, cleaning, shopping, laundry and so on."

Rochel smiled. "I enjoy designing clothes for my children but I never seem to find the time for it!" she said. "Do you mean to say that if I schedule it in first I will have a chance of fitting it into my day?"

"Yes, schedule important activities first but make sure to leave time between activities. When scheduling, one of the keys to success is the time management rule: Don't crowd your agenda; always allow for a small break between activities. And be flexible," I emphasized.

"What I mean to say is this: suppose, for instance, you've allotted one hour for sewing. You've almost finished cutting out the pattern and your hour is up. It's very difficult to stop in the middle and put everything away. If you have given yourself extra time between activities you can finish cutting out the pattern and then stop working. What if you need even more time for this project? Ask yourself, if I postpone the next item on my schedule for fifteen minutes, how will it affect the rest of my day? If it is impossible to continue because, say, you have to pick up your little one from nursery school, then it is better to stop sewing before you continue cutting another part of the pattern, to prevent the frustration of being left right in the middle of an activity."

Rochel nodded in understanding.

Satisfied that Rochel had the idea, I switched to a different topic. "There is another trick I would like to share with you: plan activities consecutively. For example, after shopping for groceries, stop in at the bank next door to check on your account or make a deposit. When you sit down to write a letter, dash off a few short notes to others as well. With just a little more planning you can accomplish a great deal."

"That rings a bell," Rochel volunteered. "I organize lectures in my neighborhood, and numerous calls must be made before each meeting. Instead of calling each woman at different times in the day I should sit down and make all of the calls at one time. If one woman's phone line is busy I can call someone else in the meantime. And if I really want to save time, I can make a list of each woman's name and telephone number instead of flipping through my phone book each time."

"Right," I answered. "But only if you can block out the time to do this. If this is impossible, your only solution may be to spread out the calls over the course of the day."

"What do you mean when you say to 'block out' time?" Rochel asked.

"Blocking out time allows you to make maximum use of a specific time slot," I explained. "It entails setting aside a chunk of your morning, afternoon or evening when you are least likely to be disturbed, and completing all or part of a project. However, many women find it impossible to find a large block of time free of interruptions. By breaking down an activity into smaller parts, and using smaller time slots, big strides can be made. For example, if a woman wants to sew a dress, she can divide and subdivide the task into smaller parts until it can be fit into even the busiest schedule.

"Another client of mine never found enough time to clean an entire room so I taught her to break it down into individual tasks. To be done over the course of the day were: 1. making the beds; 2. vacuuming; 3. washing the windows and gradually completing the room. Any job can be broken down in this way."

✌§ Interruptions

"I'm getting a feel for these new techniques in negotiating my time," Rochel commented.

"Good," I said. "Now for the six-figure question."

"What is that going to cost?" she laughed.

"You've certainly noticed how interruptions disrupt your momentum when you're trying to accomplish something. The baby starts crying just as you've finally sprayed the oven and are ready to attack the grime, the phone rings incessantly while you're changing a diaper, the neighbor appears at the most trying time of the day."

"Um. . .handling interruptions is one of my weaker points," Rochel admitted.

"Then whenever you are interrupted, you must ask the six-figure question," I said.

"Which is?"

"Is the interruption more important than the task I am involved in, or is the task more important than the interruption? If you can answer that question quickly you have made a decision of vital importance, one that corporate executives face every day (and they get paid in the six-figure range!). Your answer is no less crucial."

"You've certainly coined some unusual expressions," she laughed.

"I'll tell you why," I said. "When you are home, and in the thick of things, I assume you won't have time to run for your notebook. Catchwords and slogans help you remember the ideas."

"You have a good point," she said. "But why should I be interrupted at all? I can just turn on my answering machine when I can't talk, or I can use a cordless phone when I want to continue working while I speak."

"I see you are catching on," I said.

❧ Procrastination

There was one more important point that I wanted to mention. "Is procrastination one of your shortcomings?" I asked Rochel.

"Only sometimes," she smiled weakly. "Like when I have to pay the bills. I just don't seem to find the time to do it. Even when I mark it down on my daily 'to-do' list, I continually push it off."

"Yes," I said, "that's procrastination." I handed her the following sheet which I give to all my clients.

❧ Overcoming Procrastination

When:

    1. We procrastinate when:
    a) It's overwhelming
    b) It's unpleasant

Why:

    2. To procrastinate — to say I'll do it later — is merely a way to alleviate our guilty conscience. We know we must do something we don't want to do, and we look for a way out, a way to rationalize avoiding the job. We say, "I'll do it later," even though in the back of our minds we know we won't get to it.

    Strange as it sounds, when we procrastinate, we maintain our self-respect. We can still look ourselves in the mirror because we have told ourselves that we still intend to perform the unpleasant task.

How to break the habit:

    3. Realize that there is no such thing as procrastination. Either we do something or we don't.

    Eliminate the phrase "I'll do it later." There is no later, there is only a specific time. Either you are doing the job right now or you will do it this evening between 8:00 and

10:00 or next Thursday morning. Write the time down in your calendar.

Getting to specifics:

4. With which tasks do you procrastinate?
When do you procrastinate?
In the beginning, middle or end of a project?
What are your internal messages?
What escape routes do you take?
Some possible solutions:
5. If the work is overwhelming, divide it into smaller projects.
6. If the work is unpleasant, do one of the following:
□ Practice doing one unpleasant thing a day (what is it going to be today?) — a terrific habit to acquire.
□ Remember that if your friend begged you to do this project you would.
□ Ask yourself, "What do I gain if I do the work? What do I lose if I don't"?
□ Decide you won't be tired until bedtime.
□ Take a leading task. For example, just pick up a rag and wipe one cabinet door. Soon you will find yourself wiping the rest of the cabinets.
□ Tell everyone you know about the project.
□ Set a reasonable deadline.
□ Hire someone to do the work for you.

☙ ☙ ☙

Rochel read the outline carefully. "Any questions?" I asked her.

"Not now," she said. "Let me try out some of your suggestions and I'll get back to you."

As Rochel was leaving she noticed my family calendar hanging on the kitchen wall. Seeing that it aroused her interest, I began to explain. "Everyone in our home pencils in any event that will affect the family — for example, weddings, birthday parties, after-school activities, classes, PTA meetings, shul dinners, doctors' appointments, the school play and anything else one of us is involved in. Thus, special events are not forgotten, and several commitments are not accidentally planned for the same evening. The older children are given their own calendars to help them keep track of chores, homework and other personal matters."

Rochel looked carefully at the calendar. "You certainly have a lot going on in your house." she remarked. Then, she burst out laughing as she read aloud the quotation I had written in the corner of the calendar: "Nothing makes a person more productive than the last minute."

As Rochel was preparing to leave, we agreed that she would call me in a week to let me know how she was progressing with her newly acquired organizational skills.

◈§ Paperwork Made Easy: The Follow-up Phone Call

A week later, she called me. "Hi, this is Rochel," the enthusiastic voice on the other end of the line said. "I wanted to let you know the good news: I've finally sat down and sewn that dress, the one I told you I was never able to find the time for. And I've started attending a class that I've always wanted to go to but never seemed to have the chance."

"That's good to hear," I said. "I'm glad you created a schedule that works for you."

"But there are still a few areas that I need to work on," she said hesitantly.

"That's fine," I assured her. "There will always be areas that need improvement, refinement and change. Our hectic lives, especially with children, are not stagnant and require careful thought and planning."

"I'm happy to hear that I shouldn't expect instant success overnight," she said. "Now, to let you know what worked and what didn't: I regularly write down ideas on my master list, which is in my week-at-a-glance calendar. I've scheduled time for cleaning and for my other activities. I've posted a big family calendar on my fridge. All of these habits have boosted my efficiency. But my problem is that my master list is becoming longer and longer. I have things I'd like to do now and goals I want to achieve sometime in the future. I also have lists and lists of other things — bills to be paid, shopping lists, project ideas, and so on. I'm having trouble using such a big, bulky list."

"Well, it sounds as if there are really two questions here," I said. "One is what belongs on the master list and where to keep that which doesn't. The other, is how to achieve your larger goals and dreams.

"I can answer the first question over the phone; we can discuss the second one during our next appointment." I went on to discuss the master list in more detail. "Your master list should contain immediate projects and goals. If you have other project ideas and larger goals you might want to write them down in a separate notebook. This notebook can be divided into sections, such as: 1) meal planning and menus; 2) Yomim Tovim; 3) storage lists for all the items stored too high for you to see easily; 4) projects (if you're redecorating a room, for example, you can keep information here); 5) your dream goals — projects you would like to undertake one day; 6) lists of activities for the children; and 7) names of books and *sefarim* you want to buy or borrow. There are many other potential uses for your notebook; it simply depends on what you want to put into it. The real advantage to having such a notebook is that all the information you need is in one place. And it doesn't have to be bulky. Mine is small enough to fit into a large purse."

"It sounds as if you create a lot of paperwork recording all that information," Rochel said.

"Not at all," I replied. "Actually I save time and paperwork. For instance, when I'm sick, my husband can pick up my notebook and find my shopping list and the addresses and phone numbers of the grocery stores we use. I don't spend hours looking for scraps of paper with important information on them. I don't have to unpack all of my boxes in the basement every year to find the *succah* decorations, the Purim costumes or the size seven boys' clothes. It's all listed. Most important, the lists are safe and secure in a notebook — they don't get lost, so I don't have to rewrite them."

"Your explanation is great," Rochel said. "Now I understand how using a notebook can really save time and effort."

"As for genuine paperwork such as bills, ads that I want to keep, medical papers, and important documents, I use an expanding file folder divided into sections: medical records, leases, deeds, vacation ideas, correspondence, electricity and phone bills, and so on. As for upcoming bills and letters that need to be answered, I clip them on my calendar. Once I take care of them I file them away."

"Sounds too easy."

"I'll show it to you when you come to our next meeting. Is Monday night at 7:30 good for you?"

"Yes, I'll see you then," she said. "Thank you."

·ᴥ§ Goal Setting — The Golden Path to Success

Rochel arrived early for our meeting. Her eyes sparkling, she took out her new appointment book and master list. "I've been looking forward to this. You've given me hope that I can now turn my dreams into reality."

"I'm also looking forward to our meeting. Let's get started. A review of goal-setting principles should help you on your way." I took a deep breath and launched into the lecture I'd given so many times before. "The way we use our time should express our life's purpose. Not only do important moments make our life meaningful, but also our life's purpose makes our activities important. Cleaning and cooking gain a higher meaning when you remember the overall picture. They are only tools for achieving the goal of making our home a representation of who we are. When we know and remember our overall life purpose, we gain satisfaction and pleasure even from the small steps."

"Absolutely," Rochel said. "But when I'm drowning in a sea of housework, my vision blurs."

"You are right; most of us feel that way. But when we set goals, our vision clears. First, we must establish long-term goals. Then we set short-term goals which advance us towards the long-term ones. For example, in order to gain control of one's speech, which is a long-term goal, you need to take small steps to get there. Attending lectures, studying the laws of *shemiras haloshon* and discussing these *halachos* with close friends are small steps leading down the path to success.

"Setting a goal clarifies the picture of what we want to accomplish, and subsequently, we can chart our progress. Goals keep us on track when we are tempted to get involved in too many projects."

"I never realized just how important goal-setting really is," Rochel remarked with surprise.

"But it only works when the goal is realistic," I responded. "The goal must be challenging enough for you to want to accomplish it, yet it must still be within your range of abilities. It should be what you *want* to do, not what you *think* you should do, or what others want you to do. New goals must be consistent and compatible with other goals you have already set."

Rochel sighed deeply. "I guess becoming a supermom and career woman with a spotless house is a bit unrealistic." We both laughed.

"Now, let me give you the guidelines for goal-setting." I handed her a sheet of paper with the following printed on it:

~§ Guidelines for Goal-Setting

Goals cover every aspect of your life, physically and spiritually.

1. A goal should be written down in clear, concise language. Writing it down creates a commitment.
2. A goal should be stated in the positive, and preferably, as if you have already achieved it. (See examples below.)
3. A goal should include guidelines which clearly state when the goal will be completed and what constitutes success.
4. A goal must be something within your control.

Example I
Long-range goal: I am in control of my speech.

Short-term goals:
1. a) To buy a book on *shemiras halashon*
   b) To learn the *halachos* for 10 minutes every morning after *davening*.
   c) To finish one chapter a week.
2. To listen to a taped *shiur* on *hilchos shemiras halashon* once a week on Monday nights.

❀　❀　❀

Example II
Long-range goal: I am a responsible mother.

Short-term goals:
1. To serve nutritious meals
2. To read to my children
3. To play with my children
4. To educate my children, not just punish them
5. To speak softly
   Each of these can then be broken down into specific small steps.

❀　❀　❀

Example III
Long-range goal: I am physically fit.

Short-term goal:
1. To lose five pounds by Pesach
2. I will exercise 20 minutes every morning
3. I will use my diet plan

❀　❀　❀

After Rochel studied the sheet, I elaborated. "Once you have set your goals, plan how you will achieve them. This is how you do it. First, take your appointment book and write down the long-range goal. Second, write down the short-range goal. Third, write down the steps you can take to achieve it. Fourth, write down when you will start.

"Let's take the example of upgrading your parenting skills. You would write:

I. I am a responsible mother
    a) I will serve nutritious meals every day
        1. I will call my friend Leora who cooks healthy food and has good ideas: Call Monday evening
        2. I will buy a kosher health-oriented cookbook: Buy Wednesday A.M.
        3. I will write a menu plan for the week: Write every Sunday
        4. I will shop in the health food store: Shop once a week

"If you can't think of any goals you want to strive for, then ask yourself the following questions: How would I like to be tomorrow? Ten years from now? Twenty years from now? On my sixtieth birthday? Sometimes, it helps to brainstorm with pen and paper. The more specific and real a goal is to you, the more likely you are to achieve it. Sometimes, it helps to envision yourself having already attained your goal. For example, imagine yourself having control over your speech. Picture yourself reacting in a calm, cool manner in all situations."

I sat back for a moment. Rochel appeared to be deep in thought. Finally, she said, "I can't wait to try this out. I feel that now I possess the skills to achieve my goals." She gathered her belongings and thanked me enthusiastically. As we said goodbye, I reflected on my own inner happiness at being able to help other women achieve their goals; it was once only a dream of mine — today it's a reality.

◄§ Beating Burnout

Rivka couldn't figure it out. She'd read books on household organization and time management. She was as organized as a working mother could hope to be. Then why did she always feel as if she were fighting a losing battle against the clock? Lately, it was as if she lived in a pressure cooker whose steam valve was clamped shut, and all the pressure was building up inside. At any moment the lid might pop off and explode. She was having headaches and backaches on a regular basis and was often too tired to even eat a decent meal. Coffee and cake were all that was digestable. "What am I doing wrong?" she muttered under her breath as she began to wash a sink full of dishes. Before she could stop herself, she was daydreaming about a vacation, until she realized that she'd been rinsing the same dish for a few minutes.

The phone rang, shaking her out of her reverie. It was her friend Rochel. During their conversation, Rochel described her time-management consultation and suggested that the new skills she'd learned could help her too. Rivka became impatient. "I don't know if you noticed, but I am a punctual person," she said. "I use my calendar regularly. I don't think that I have a problem managing my time — I simply don't have enough of it!"

❈ ❈ ❈

A few days later I received a call from Rivka, who made an appointment with me. "I'm an organized person," she said. "I work part-time. I do all my own baking and cooking. I clean my house thoroughly on a regular basis. Then why do I feel like I'm failing? Is there something else I should be doing?"

"It sounds to me as if you are doing too much," I answered her. "Instead of working harder, I think you must rest more to restore your energy."

"What?" Rivka cut in, incredulous. "I barely have time for the sewing, the ironing and the rest of the chores. Now you are telling me to rest *more?*"

"Absolutely," I responded. "We need a lot of physical energy to take care of our families. Just as important, we need to set a good example for our children by taking good care of ourselves. Why should we expect our children to sit down to eat three healthy meals when they see us drinking a cup of coffee and grabbing a chocolate bar for lunch? Why should they brush their hair when we don't take the time to do it?

"I'm not suggesting we hire full-time cleaning and cooking help and spend our days pampering ourselves. What I *am* suggesting is that there has to be a balance, because if we don't take care of ourselves then we will have less energy for our husbands, our children and our homes. Let me illustrate my point: the U.S. Army once did an experiment which has been repeated and verified since. They divided army recruits into two groups, each one assigned to do the same amount of physical labor. The difference between them was that one group rested for fifteen minutes after each hour of work. The other group worked for three hours straight and then had a long rest break. The result? The group that rested more frequently produced better results than the one that worked for three hours before taking a break."

I paused to let the importance of my proof sink in, but Rivka didn't seem convinced. "That is hard for me to believe," she said skeptically.

"Yes, it does sound illogical," I admitted, "but that is how our bodies work. We need to rest in order to renew our strength. When we feel rested we have more energy, patience and peace of mind. A lot of energy is wasted when we get nervous and annoyed. When we're calm, we usually do a better job of taking care of our families. More often than not they respond positively."

"I've noticed that with my own family," Rivka said. "When I'm having a good day, the children seem to have a good day. When I'm feeling miserable, they are impossible to reason with. After I rest I concentrate better. But if I'm exhausted I walk around in circles — I'm simply unable to remember what I should be doing." While Rivka reflected on her experiences I made us both a cup of tea.

"So how do I find time to rest and still accomplish all my endless tasks?" she asked me.

"Well, you've just taken the first step, which is acknowledging your own limitations," I replied. "It means recognizing that Hashem gave you this situation and that you can deal with it and still find time to take care of yourself. *U'shemartem es nafshose-ichem*, guarding your health, is a *mitzvah* in the Torah. As with all other *mitzvos*, we have a *yetzer hara* which tries to make us transgress this.

"Some women burn out slowly," I went on. "They get caught up in housework and family, leaving no time for themselves. Soon they lack energy and motivation. They admit that they don't know what keeps them so busy everyday but somehow, they never finish. This type of woman needs to concentrate on a neglected area (like sewing) and curtail work on another area (like scrubbing the light fixtures). Changing one's focus can be refreshing. Other women need to add a *shiur* or an exercise class to their schedules. The change in routine will revitalize them.

"Then, there are the superwomen. They have to do it all: perfect mother, *balabusta,* career lady, *chesed* organizer. After a while these activities take their toll. This type of woman is the most likely candidate for burnout. To avoid it, she must cut down somewhere. If her husband prefers fresh meals everyday, as opposed to reheated leftovers, this should NOT be eliminated. But it doesn't mean that extra help can't be brought in to help her with the cleaning and cooking. Other housekeeping shortcuts can be implemented too."

Rivka stopped me mid-lecture. "Can you give me a few hints?"

I started with my favorite target. "First and foremost, one has to give up perfectionism. This affliction is harmful in any area but especially when it comes to housework." Rivka flashed me a knowing smile.

"For example," I continued, "corners don't encounter much traffic, so they don't have to be attacked every day with a mop. Concentrate instead on areas with high traffic flow. This is the professional method; most cleaning crews clean heavily used areas daily but corners only twice a month! Prevention is another golden rule. Eliminate dirt from your threshold by using high quality mats outside each door. This will keep people from tracking dirt into your house. Whenever you're doing anything messy, put down dropcloths or old newspapers and move everything out of the way. Better yet, throw out all the junk cluttering your house. Then you won't have to move it *or* clean it. Windows and walls can be washed on an infrequent basis, and let the dish drainer dry your dishes. What do you think?"

"Your ideas sound interesting," Rivka replied, "but I'm afraid I'll set a bad example for the children."

"Listen, Rivka," I said, "I've heard children lament that their mothers spent so much time cooking and cleaning, they were too exhausted to give them attention. But I never heard any children complain about an energetic and happy mother who gave them cereal and milk for supper."

Rivka smiled. I'd scored a point. "But what should I do," she asked, "when the neighborhood *chesed* committee needs someone to make phone calls or pick up groceries for housebound elderly people or bake cakes for the PTA? The list is endless," she finished, letting out a sigh.

"Remember that each and every one of us is limited. We all have only a certain amount of time and energy." Rivka nodded in agreement.

"So it makes sense to focus on what you're capable of doing, given your individual time constraints and energy level," I said. "That means, don't take on an assignment which will give your family the impression that you've disappeared. Or, if you have a weak back, then I would not advise you to carry groceries for the elderly. Consider instead making a friendly phone call to an elderly person, or giving *tzedakah* cheerfully when a collector comes to your door or even offering a friendly word to a neighbor whose spirits seem low. It's all a matter of considering your options," I explained.

Rivka shot me a determined look. "I want to set aside a specific block of time each week to help the local *chesed* committee," she said. "I just have to make sure that I don't take on more work than I can handle!"

"This must be your attitude towards all of your responsibilities," I said. "Taking on too much at home or in the office is a sure way to run yourself into the ground. A major signal of burnout is when you feel that any request, no matter how small, is simply too much to deal with and you end up resenting the appeal. This is a sign that a restructuring of your commitments is in order. So start by making a list of every activity you are currently involved in. Then look through the list to see which jobs you can eliminate, either temporarily or permanently."

Rivka started to make a list in her notebook. As she was writing, I interrupted her. "Now, do you have any ideas on how to actually lighten your workload?"

After a few minutes of reflection, Rivka answered, "I'll send out my ironing for the next two months and I'll simplify my cooking by relying on easier meals, as you suggested in your meal planning pamphlet. I'll try some of your housekeeping shortcuts and I'll enlist my children's help with the rest. If that won't do, I'll get extra help on a temporary basis. But most importantly, I'll eat healthy meals and take time out to enjoy the children."

STEP TWO — AT A GLANCE

1. Use a weekly appointment book.

2. Make a list of all of your activities and responsibilities and divide them into three categories: a) important to you; b) must be done by you; c) to be delegated or eliminated.

3. Transfer all activities you will be doing yourself to a master list.

4. Take into account your physical and mental energy levels at various times in the day when assigning a task to a specific time.

5. When scheduling from the master list into the appointment book, first schedule appointments (such as doctor, dentist, and the like) then schedule in "a" items, then "b" items (important and necessary).

---

6. Time specific activities so that you have a realisitic idea of how long it takes you, for example, to drive to the pharmacy, go shopping at the local grocery store, pay the phone bill, and so on.

7. Don't overload your schedule. Leave some blocks of time free.

8. Rest between chores.

9. Plan similar activities at the same time of the day and plan activities located together for the same block of time.

10. Block out time for large projects or break them down into small manageable steps.

11. Don't let interruptions spoil your plan.

12. Postpone procrastination.

13. Hang up a calendar to keep track of family activities.

14. Make a notebook for: a) meal plans and menus; b) chaggim; c) storage lists; d) projects; e) dream goals.

15. Store all bills and documents in an expanding file folder and keep in a convenient location.

16. Goal setting helps you clarify what you want to accomplish and charts your progress. To set a goal, you must write down: a) long-range goal; b) short-range goal; c) steps to achieve goal; d) starting date or time period given to accomplish goal.

17. To avoid burnout: a) look for housekeeping shortcuts; b) change routine — add a new class or project or drop an inconvenient one; c) rearrange cleaning schedule; d) prioritize activities and temporarily or permanently drop extras; e) take good care of yourself: eat healthy meals and get enough sleep.

Step Three
Systematic Cleaning

I t's normal for a wife and mother to feel tired, to get bogged down in housework, to serve simple meals. But I feel simply inadequate compared to my neighbor. . .

My neighbor is the ideal wife.

She is awake and dressed before her husband. Breakfast is ready promptly after *davening*. She awaits her husband's arrival at night, appearing neat and attractive. Tempting aromas beckon from the kitchen. After dinner, she escorts him to the door with an encouraging word as he leaves for his night *seder*. In the closet hang his crisply ironed shirts, (matching) buttons are firmly in place, and tears and rips are expertly mended. She holds down a part-time job and has devised innumerable schemes for saving money. Not a penny is spent on wig styling or children's haircuts. Her distinctive flair earns her a local reputation.

My neighbor is an outstanding housewife.

Her floors sparkle twenty-four hours a day. Dust and dirt dare not enter her door (why should they when they are so comfortable in *my* home?). From her bathrooms wafts the delicate scent of roses. Her pots and pans gleam. The furniture looks brand-new. She never runs out of milk or discovers at candle lighting time that she forgot to buy candles.

My neighbor is the perfect cook.

She prepares nutritious hot breakfasts, lunches and dinners every day including *erev Shabbos*, Yom Tov, and Pesach. She never burns the rice. In her capable hands even Pesach cakes don't flop. She even bakes her own challahs, grows her own vegetables and *kashers* her own chickens.

My neighbor has a knack for organization.

She carefully packs away her *succah* decorations from year to year. She finds time to sew clothing for the children and herself. She heads the PTA and is active in five different *chesed* organizations.

My neighbor is an exemplary mother.

Her children arrive at school punctually at eight o'clock on the dot. She is available to them every evening to help them with their homework. The carpool relies heavily on her participation. The Chanukah party wouldn't be complete without her famous dreidel shaped cake. She is never too busy to make star charts to encourage good behavior in her children and is a regular participant at the weekly parenting class. She rarely raises her voice; nevertheless, obedience is the banner of her household.

And you wonder why I'm feeling overwhelmed?

ᴥ Two Views

Most of us grow up with externally imposed schedules telling us when to eat, when to *daven*, when to study, when to work, when to clean, and so forth. Then one day we marry and are expected to be time management experts, juggling home, family and the other myriad responsibilities that accompany marriage. Often coming to the job with little training or experience, we are expected to become proficient at housekeeping, cooking, decorating, entertaining and every other task associated with being an *akeres habayis*. We are left wondering how and when we are going to manage to accomplish everything.

Even though we have so much to do, it is only our husbands and children who possess established schedules — we have more flexibility. Therefore, we might leave our "jobs" unscheduled, hoping they'll take care of themselves, or we might get easily distracted and switch from chore to chore without ever finishing one of them. Yet it seems silly to actually "schedule" cooking, cleaning and the rest. We just scrape through one way or another.

Could there be a better way? Every woman tends to ask herself this question, especially after a rough day. To answer it, let's examine an average day in the life of two neighbors, Mashi and Bashi.

Mashi's Story

A new day has dawned in the Weissfeld household. Breathless from the fast pace of getting everyone ready in the morning, Mashi enters the kitchen to survey the damage. A tub of soft cheese is overturned on the floor, two plastic bags are on the chair, the children's hairbrushes are on the counter and the remnants of packed lunches past, at which she would rather not look, are on the kitchen table. She picks up the junk from the floor and clears and wipes the table. Deciding to leave the rest for later, she goes to the bedroom to get dressed. On the way, she notices some toys and the pages of the newspaper strewn across the living room carpet. It looks so messy that she can't bear to pass it by, so she straightens out the newspaper, page by page, then scoops up the toys and deposits them in the bedroom toy box, only to discover the children hadn't made their beds. That certainly won't do; she carefully makes each one. Satisfied, she finally returns to her bedroom. But horror of horrors, she eyes her husband's dirty socks huddled in a corner of the room, along with his undershirt and work shirt. And the pants he had hung on the closet door have fallen down and lay crumpled on the floor. So she picks up all the dirty clothes and carries them to the hamper downstairs in the basement. When she returns, she picks up her husband's pants, and she notices a large rip in the seat. "Hmm. . . when will I mend this?" she wonders out loud.

Mashi dresses and *davens*. When she finishes, she looks at her watch — ten o'clock already! Her stomach growls. To her great disappointment she observes that there are no clean dishes or silverware. She grabs an apple and begins the assault on the sink. The phone rings. "Hi, Mash, it's me, Devorah. Just wanted to schmooze a bit. Got some time?" Unable to resist, Mashi nestles the phone on her shoulder and washes the dishes as she talks. Finding it difficult to hang up, she continues speaking even after the dishes are done. After a long conversation, she realizes that Heshi will be returning from play group soon and there is still so much to be done. When she finally says goodbye, she throws a load of laundry into the washing machine and starts to cook lunch. On today's menu: potato blintzes. While she is still frying the blintzes, Heshi dashes through the door. She kisses him hello and hurries back to her frying pan. She is beginning to get tired but she can't slow down now. After finishing the blintzes she washes the newly dirtied dishes and then goes into the bedroom to mend her husband's ripped pants. Heshi gets bored drawing with crayons and so she sends him to play in the backyard. Just then the girls come home. As they run into the kitchen, she notices with dismay that they have tracked mud across the floor. With last night's hard work in mind, Mashi hauls out the mop and once again cleans the kitchen floor thoroughly. The girls call out to her from the kitchen and she sits down to talk with them. Although it seems like only minutes have passed, when she glances at the kitchen clock she is startled to discover that her husband will be home in fifteen minutes — and he doesn't like potato blintzes!

Cooking will take too much time, so she loads the children into the car and speeds to the delicatessen to buy cold cuts. After a somewhat lengthy wait in line she reaches home — only twenty minutes after her husband arrives. But he is in a good mood anyway and they all sit down to enjoy the impromptu supper. She finally puts the children to bed and returns to the living room to finish the discussion she was having with her husband. When he leaves to go to a *shiur* she surveys with consternation the topsy-turvy house and wonders where the day went.

Bashi's Story

Bashi wakes up early. She dresses and begins to *daven* in the quiet stillness of the morning. While she *davens*, the children get up and find their mother at prayer. They don't want to disturb her so they take out a few toys and play quietly by themselves. After she finishes, she brings the baby a bottle and starts to prepare breakfast. As the older ones get dressed, Bashi checks on everyone to see how they are doing. She pushes a shirt over a head and pulls a sock onto a foot. Each child eats breakfast, takes his lunch box and leaves the house in plenty of time before the school bus arrives.

As Bashi eats breakfast, she reminisces about what her life was like before she'd gone to the home management seminar she had attended because she was fed up with making lists and losing lists, searching for a clean shirt five minutes before the school bus arrived, and suffering through her children's cries of hunger while she was beginning to cook lunch. She had been over-whelmed by too much work and not enough time. And now she was sitting down to a leisurely breakfast after having found time to *daven*. Things weren't always perfect but they were running smoothly; she had a feeling of being on top of the house and not the other way around. She'd even found time to oil paint, a dream she had thought she would never realize.

Assessing the reasons for her new-found success, she realizes that the seminar's personalized home management system is what made such an impact on her life. In the beginning it had been difficult to keep to a cleaning schedule. Her neighbors all seemed to clean naturally; they certainly didn't use any schedules. But now that she has a written list of chores they no longer run around in her head, each screaming for attention. Bashi doesn't worry about undone household tasks because she knows each one is scheduled. No longer does she start the first task in sight and then become distracted by something else. She finishes each job one at a time. Each chore is written down, completed and then forgotten. Bashi feels as though she is working smarter instead of harder.

Bashi takes out her schedule. Today is Monday, her big cleaning day. She enjoys having two cleaning days, Monday and Friday. During the rest of the week she does basic maintenance. Another woman she had met in the seminar expressed her preference for cleaning an hour each day and another friend admitted to cleaning early in the morning before her children woke up. The consultants had stressed the importance of each woman developing her own personalized system catered to her own needs and special priorities.

Bashi had been happy to learn that she no longer had to vacuum every inch of the house. She could vacuum the most frequently used areas twice a week and vacuum under the couch once a month. After all, no one was going to inspect her home. She was encouraged to live up to her *own* standards, not someone else's or some imaginary ones. It had taken time to organize her house, but she had done it, one step at a time. Bashi experimented with her schedule to discover what worked and what didn't. She learned to group similar tasks together to keep her momentum going. For example, when she washed dishes, she also cleaned the sink and wiped down the tiles and the table instead of making a separate trip to the kitchen to do those jobs. Using a "clean-as-you-go" system instead of a "pick-it-up-and-stop" methodology, she was able to do more in less time. Previously, cleaning a room meant going in and out with one item at a time. Now she collects each item that belongs somewhere else and puts it in a box; when she leaves the room she takes the box with her.

Although Bashi still has some of "those days" when everything seems to go wrong, she doesn't become upset because she always manages to accomplish her minimum goals. Most importantly, Bashi takes regular rest breaks to recoup her energy. She used to feel guilty each time she sat down, but no longer! She now knows that a woman won't work efficiently if she isn't rested.

Bashi takes out her notes from the seminar. As she reviews her list of good cleaning habits, she muses over how she used to be and how far she has come. Her neighbor wasn't the only one to be privy to such useful information.

The following section is a copy of the lecture Bashi attended.

✑ Your Personalized Home Management System

Do you have a habit of keeping your unexpected guests standing in the hallway while you and your children quickly put things in order? Do you feel like hiding when your in-laws come for a visit? Or does your living room always appear tidy because you never allow any family member to set foot in it?

Have you decided to solve all your cleaning problems by setting up a tent in the back yard and moving your children there permanently? Or are you a good home manager looking for an even more efficient method? Whatever your situation may be, a home management system will improve your efficiency and help you achieve your household goals. Not all women share the same vision of what their homes should look like, nor do they all share the same feelings about cleaning. Therefore, each woman has to evaluate her own desires and needs. A personalized home management system is the tool that enables you to clean your house in an organized and systematic fashion based on your family's needs.

But why use a written household cleaning schedule instead of the good old-fashioned method of cleaning whenever you wish to scrub, depending upon whatever less-than-sparkling object you happen to notice at the time? Well, here are a few convincing reasons. Five are listed here, although you might be able to think of more.

1. **A written schedule,** in which all your chores are written down and assigned a specific time slot, keeps those unfinished jobs from swimming around in your thoughts. You don't have to constantly ask yourself when "x" will get done. My theory is: Write it, do it and forget it.
2. **A written schedule** helps you to avoid the temptation to do other jobs that catch your attention, because you know that any task you deem important is marked down and has a time set aside for it.
3. **A written schedule** reduces procrastination, because once you get into the swing of things, a new rhythm is created which helps keep you moving.
4. **A written schedule** makes delegating chores easier, because if you are unable to continue cleaning, you know exactly what job to delegate to a cleaning woman or to a young volunteer.
5. **A written schedule** helps you to wisely plan other appointments. For example, on heavy cleaning days you won't slate a shopping expedition.

In order to develop your own efficient system you must decide which tasks are your priorities, which tasks would be nice to have finished, and which tasks can be avoided altogether. Below I will ask you some questions to help you determine your priorities. Don't compare yourself with others. Just because your neighbor dusts her house every day doesn't mean that you must do likewise. Each family is different, each house is different, and each woman has her own *meshugas!* Keep in mind your husband's preferences, too. If he dislikes walking into the kitchen and seeing a messy table, then having the table cleared early in the evening will appear on your list of priorities.

✑ Determining Priorities — The Minimum, the Preferred, and the Maximum

Because each house differs as to the number of people living there, the ages of its occupants, the building material used in its construction, the type of furnishings and appliances, and various other factors, each woman will have different priorities. If, for example, a family of six owns a set of dishes for six, then washing the dishes will be a high priority. If the living room also doubles as a bedroom, then making the beds each morning will be a high priority. If you don't have children, then there is no real need to sweep the floors every day, but if you live in a construction area then you might consider it. Therefore, assess your current household situation and answer the following questions. (When answering the questions keep in mind that you are trying to determine what must be done, not whether you will be the one to do it.)

Worksheet #1 — Priorities

The following questions will help you determine the minimum number of household chores needed to keep your house afloat. Rank the tasks in order of importance.

1. *What is the absolute minimum that must be done each day?*
   Beds, dishes, general pickup, sweep, take out trash, wash and dry laundry, put away laundry, wash floors, other

2. *What is the absolute minimum that must be done each week? How many times a week?*
   Beds, dishes, general pickup, sweep, wash and dry laundry,

put away laundry, wash floors, take out trash, iron, vacuum, other

The following questions will help you determine the preferred number of household chores to be done in order to maintain a good-looking house. Rank them in order of importance.

3. *What would I like to have done in my house each day?*
   Beds, dishes, general pickup, sweep, wash and dry laundry, put away laundry, wash floors, other

4. *What would I like to have done in my house each week? How many times a week?*
   Beds, dishes, general pickup, sweep, wash and dry laundry, put away laundry, wash floors, take out trash, iron, vacuum, other

The following questions will help you determine the maximum number of household chores needed to keep your house looking like a museum. Rank them in order of importance.

5. *If I had the time, the energy, or unlimited cleaning help, what would be the maximum number of times each task should be done every day?*
   Beds, dishes, general pickup, sweep, wash and dry laundry, put away laundry, wash floors, other

6. *What would be the maximum number of times each task should be done every week?*
   Beds, dishes, general pickup, sweep, wash and dry laundry, put away laundry, wash floors, take out trash, iron, vacuum, other

With the above information written down you must evaluate your own situation. If you have the money to hire a full-time housekeeper or the energy and the desire to see your house sparkle like the king's jewels, then your goal will be to create a cleaning schedule based on your maximum needs. If you have some help in the home and you work part-time, then creating a cleaning schedule based on the preferred number of household chores might be the goal to work towards. If you are pregnant with your fourth child and your oldest is four and you're on a tight budget, then creating a schedule based on your minimum needs might be your best bet.

Based on your decision to follow a minimum, preferred or maximum schedule, fill out the following two worksheets.

Worksheet #2 — Household Tasks

Next to each task write down how often you would like to see it done: daily, twice a week, weekly, monthly, or quarterly.

Write down which day of the week (or month) you will do it and what time of day: morning, afternoon, evening.

For any tasks you will not perform personally but want to see done, write the name of the person responsible for doing it next to the task. Before delegating a task to your husband or children, ask them their preferences. You might be pleasantly surprised.

TASK	HOW OFTEN	DATE	WHEN	WHO
beds				
change sheets				
clean behind/under fridge				
clean behind/under stove				
clean drapes				
clean fridge				
clean garage				
clean laundry room				
clean oven				
clean porch				
clean radiators				
clean sofa and chairs				
clean stove top				
clean toilets				
clean wall near stove				
defrost freezer				
dishes				

TASK	HOW OFTEN	DATE	WHEN	WHO
dry laundry				
empty bathroom trash				
empty bedroom trash				
fold/put away laundry				
general pickup				
iron				
kitchen trash				
mend clothes				
plan weekly schedule				
polish silver				
scrub bathroom sink				
scrub bathtub				
shop for nonperishables				
shop for perishables				
shop for fruits/vegetables				
straighten closets				
straighten drawers				
sweep kitchen				
vacuum bedroom				
vacuum hall				
vacuum living room				
vacuum sofa and chairs				
wash bathroom floor				
wash carpet				
wash kitchen floor				
wash kitchen walls				
wash laundry (adults)				
wash laundry (children)				
wash darks				
wash lights				
wash other walls				
wash windows				
water plants				
write letters				

✑ Worksheet #3 — Cleaning Schedule

Transfer information from household task sheet onto this schedule for easy reference

	SUNDAY	MONDAY	TUESDAY	WEDNESDAY	THRUSDAY	FRIDAY	MOTZ. SHAB.
MORN.							
AFT.							
EVE.							

First Week of the Month: _____

Second Week of the Month: _____

Third Week of the Month: _____

Fourth Week of the Month: _____

Special Projects: _____

✑ Getting Down to Business

Now that you have created your own personalized schedule, let's go on to the actual cleaning. You have a number of choices here too. What will your standard of cleanliness be? But before you decide, I will let you in on a little secret. You don't always have to do a perfect job. After all, chances are, whatever you've cleaned will just get dirty within another twenty-four hours anyway. So, will you do a below average job (I won't tell anybody), an average job, or an above average job? How much time will you spend on each chore? How much time will you spend cleaning altogether? When will quitting time be? (Yes, we all need to take breaks!)

In order to stick to your new schedule, you must decide what you will do if you find it difficult to fit in all of the chores you have scheduled for that day. Look at your schedule on worksheet #3, to make sure you have completed the tasks that are most important to you. If a task remains unfinished and it is one of the more important items on your list, you must decide whether to push off something else you had planned to accomplish and do a good job on the task at hand, or to simply perform the important chore as quickly as possible even though your results will be less than perfect. For example, you were supposed to vacuum the bedroom carpet in the morning before you went vegetable shopping, but a neighbor dropped by to visit during that time and now you have to leave. So you can either vacuum the rug quickly and not do as thorough a job as you wanted to, or you can vacuum it completely and save the shopping for later. Never skip the job completely for your written schedule is a contract. Once you break that contract you might find yourself playing hooky more and more often. So keep the momentum going; if you have to lower your standards, then lower them in these types of situations.

Another trick to remember is to "clean as you go." If you are washing your dishes, for instance, then clean out the sink and wipe down the tiles too. Since you are in the kitchen anyway, the task will go more quickly than if you make a special trip to the kitchen just to wash the sink. Likewise, wash the outside of the fridge and the door when you are wiping down the kitchen cabinets. If the rag is in your hand anyway, then why not? You will only waste precious minutes by setting aside a special time to clean the kitchen door.

Prevention is also an important word in the Jewish home-maker's vocabulary. Eliminate extra work by wearing a housecoat when serving food or feeding children. Put bibs on every child during meals. Place mats outside the front door and any other doors leading from the outside to the inside of your house. One client of mine confessed that she hardly ever had to wash her floors because she made every member of the family take off their shoes and put on slippers each time they entered the house.

If you have thirty minutes to straighten up your home, why waste the time running from room to room? Create a system for general pickup. When unexpected visitors come, what part of the house do they see first? More often than not, they see the front door first. Therefore make sure that toys, trash and forgotten items don't accumulate there. Next comes the front hall. Does it have a tidy appearance? Once you've taken care of these areas, you decide what should be the order of priority: the living room, bathroom, kitchen, or bedrooms. Whatever you decide, create a straightening-up routine so that it becomes quick and easy. For a fast cleanup, clear off surfaces such as tables, sofa, chairs, kitchen countertops. Then clear passageways of clutter. It is amazing how much more organized the house looks after a quick pickup even when no thorough cleaning was done. This is a very potent psychological weapon; once your house looks cleaner you will feel better and you can go on to deeper cleaning, or on to something else, without feeling guilty.

Easier said than done, you are probably muttering. What would you say about the following scenario? You are in the middle of cooking up a storm when you leave the kitchen to attend to a crying child. As you step back into the kitchen you discover that you have left it in a state of chaos worthy of a call to the U.S. Goverment's Disaster Relief Service. What should you do first, you ask? I will tell you, as I tell each and every client: Look through an imaginary telescope. Instead of surveying the entire kitchen in one glance, just focus on one place at a time. Start with the kitchen table. It might be cluttered with dishes, a pot, children's drawings, a vase and a letter from a friend. In your mind, separate each item into the category to which it belongs. Begin with the easiest category, which is anything destined for the garbage can. Then continue with items which belong in the *milchig* sink, the *milchig* cabinet, and so on. Assign a place for items that don't belong in the kitchen. For example, you might hang up children's drawings on a bulletin board in their bedroom; therefore place their drawings on one chair or on the corner of the counter. Just make sure you don't leave the kitchen — it will slow you down. Keep categorizing each item until the kitchen table is finished. Then clear off each counter top. Using this method of clearing up, you are sure to feel less overwhelmed.

The following is a good-cleaning-habit list. Everyone knows

what good cleaning habits are, but few of us put them into action. Fill out the following habit report:

⇝ Description

_____ seldom   _____ sometimes   _____ often

___ 1. I put an item away after I use it.
___ 2. I clean tables and counters after each meal.
___ 3. I wash off preparation dishes and utensils while I cook.
___ 4. I soak dishes and pots.
___ 5. I keep spray bottles filled with cleaning fluid in my kitchen and bathrooms for a quick clean-up.
___ 6. I pick up items as I pass by them.
___ 7. I reuse clean clothes even if they have been worn.
___ 8. I clean spills as they occur.
___ 9. I clean out my purse each time I arrive home.
___ 10. I make productive use of waiting time.
___ 11. I decide what to make for dinner the night before.
___ 12. I do one thing I don't want to do each day.

If you answered "often" to eight or more questions you are quite a *balabusta*. If you answered "often" less than eight times, or if you never answered "often," you are still O.K. in my book. I'm sure you have other wonderful qualities, so just keep plugging away!

If you find it difficult to adhere to the above good habits (or any good habit, for that matter), remember: a catchy slogan repeated over and over can work wonders. For example, if you find it difficult to put things away immediately after using them, repeat this little rhyme ten times a day:

Don't delay, put it away.

For those of you who find it difficult to get enthusiastic about cleaning, perhaps the next three questions can help you: Do you need improved cleaning tools or methods? A better broom or a speedier way to clear up each room might provide the answer.

What task would you like to make easier? Hiring extra help, convincing your husband and children to do more, or using more convenience items such as paper plates or paper towels might be the solution. Would specific household repairs or additions lighten your burden? An extra shelf or a row of hooks on the wall might help do the trick.

But the best cleaning advice of all is to rest when you are tired, or better yet, to rest *before* you get tired. This way you will have the energy to do what must be done. Just make sure to sit down between each activity. Your energy will be restored and you will work more efficiently throughout the day.

STEP THREE — AT A GLANCE

1. Get an early start.
2. Use a written schedule.
3. Determine your cleaning priorities.
4. What are your cleaning standards? Will you aim for a quick job, average job, immaculate job?
5. Establish starting and finishing times.
6. Stick to the schedule even if it means lowering standards.
7. Prevent dirt from building up. Use door mats and wipe spills as they occur.
8. Set aside time for a daily cleanup.
9. Get used to good cleaning habits.
10. Rest between tasks.

Step Four
Household
Organization

L ooking for her hat, Frieda opened the door to her children's closet and was hit on the head by a falling shoe. She quickly put up her hand and caught the pair of scissors and green cotton dress which were on their way down too. As she stuffed them back onto the shelf she wondered why the shoe was up there in the first place. Then she remembered hiding it from her daughter Suri, who loved to wear her Shabbos shoes every day. And why was there only one? Frieda couldn't find the matching shoe. She hoped it hadn't been in the pile of laundry she had just thrown into the washing machine. It was black patent leather and would surely be ruined. . .

Once again addressing herself to the problem at hand, she decided that this bump on her head was not going to deter her from finding her winter hat. It was the first really cold day of the season and she couldn't go outside without it. She had last seen it being stuffed into one of her husband's brown rain boots. Frieda vaguely recalled noticing Suri carrying them in the direction of the children's closet.

If this scenerio sounds familiar, you are not alone. How and where to store things presents a constant dilemma. In this chapter, the "where" and "how" of storage will be discussed. Long-term, short-term, kitchen pantry and toy storage will be some of the topics covered. I will also propose a system for de-cluttering your house. If you are afraid to open your closet door, or if you just want some extra tips, this chapter is for you.

·§ Item by Item

For the past few years I have been teaching the underlying principle of storage, which lies at the heart of all the organizational principles. It requires neither buying a new home, building an additional room nor even investing in fancy cabinets. (I'm not ruling out the possibility of putting in extra shelves in strategic locations. I'm simply pointing out that one needn't make any great investments in order to get organized.) When I first discovered the golden rule of organization I was shocked by its simplicity:

Make it convenient.

I can hear you laughing and saying to yourself, "It sounds too easy. Is that all there is to. it?" The answer is, yes and no. This principle is the foundation. If you are having trouble finding a place for all those homeless items, think convenience. If you iron in the bedroom, for example, then keep the iron and ironing board in the bedroom, not in the utility room. Where you use the item is where you should store it.

Of course, don't misconstrue this principle to mean that because the most convenient place to put things is on top of every counter top, table and open space, then that is where they should go. Obviously, items will be lost or misplaced if they don't have a space to call home. But instead of assigning each object an arbitrary location, think in terms of convenience.

In consultations with my clients, we consider each item separately when looking for the appropriate storage location. I've found the following five questions to be the most helpful in determining where to put things:

Question 1: Where is the item used?

Question 2: How frequently is it used?

Question 3: With what other items is it used?

Question 4: Where is the most appropriate place for it in terms of its size and the material it is made from?

Question 5: Is it easy to put away?

◄§ Question 1 — Milly Didn't Ask It

Milly stepped back to admire her hard work. Magnificent. Finally, her hall closet was organized. Not that she hadn't straightened it a dozen times before, but this time it was going to last. Each shelf was stacked high with sheets, tablecloths, towels, bibs and all the material for her future sewing projects. The closet was located "conveniently" at the far end of the hall.

Unfortunately, despite Milly's determination to keep things neat, the order had deteriorated within two weeks. Why? That is what Milly wanted to know. When I was called onto the scene I asked her where each item was used (obviously not in the hall!). The answers were straightforward: the towels were used in the bathroom, the sheets in the bedroom, the tableclothes in the dining room and the bibs in the kitchen. "So why not store them there?" I asked her.

Her eyes lit up. "I thought that the hall closet was where they were supposed to go," she admitted. Upon examining the closets in her other rooms she discovered that she had space for each item in the room in which it was used. I advised her to use the hall closet for long term storage, like sewing projects, Purim costumes, *succah* decorations, off-season storage, and anything she wanted a place for but she didn't need often. Now, when Milly looks for an area to store her things she asks herself, "Where do I use it?"

⊰ Question 2 — Chava Didn't Ask It

Chava stretched as far as she could to reach the jar of coffee on the top shelf of the pantry. Just as she felt it in her hands, it fell to the floor with a crash. "Oh no, that was my last jar of coffee," she mumbled to herself. Quickly, she cleaned up the mess and threw a coat over her shoulders, running next door to Simi's to borrow some coffee before Yanky returned home from *Shacharis*. He had just entered a new night *kollel* and came home late every night, but she stayed up to greet him. A minimum of sleep necessitated a strong dose of caffeine for her in the morning.

Returning from Simi's with the prized possession in her hands, it suddenly dawned on her that her kitchen cabinets were working against her. Nothing was ever where she needed it. A home management consultant (yours truly) was asked to survey the problem kitchen.

Opening her pantry, I pointed to the grape juice on the lower shelf and asked her how often she uses it. "On Shabbos," she replied, somewhat meekly. "But I leave it there so I won't forget where I've put it from week to week." Then I repeated my question as I pointed to each item on the shelf. It became apparent that she was wasting precious space on products she didn't use often, which forced her to store the frequently used items on a higher shelf. The broken coffee jar was a result of this illogical arrangement.

"If something is used frequently," I explained, "it should be stored in an easy to reach location, either on a shelf or hanging up within arm's length. This is called one-motion storage, because you can reach it without standing on a stool or bending down on your knees to reach deeply into a cabinet."

Chava looked puzzled. "When we moved into our home a year ago and I first organized the kitchen, everything ran smoothly. Why has it become so impractical now?" she asked. Then Chava smiled. I could see that she had already answered her own question. "I know," she said. "When we first got married I had a lot of time to *patchke* in the kitchen, and so I put all the food items I used then on a lower shelf. Now I cook meals that take less time and effort. And we drink much more coffee than we used to. Yet, I still store these things on the high shelf as I always have."

After finding a more practical place for her grape juice and the other misplaced items, Chava was satisfied with her food pantry. Now, when Chava puts her groceries back into the pantry she asks herself, "How frequently do I use this item?" and stores it in the most convenient location.

◄§ Question 3 — Dina Didn't Ask It

Dina's brother and sister-in-law were sitting in the dining room, patiently waiting for her to emerge from the kitchen. "Oh, why didn't they call first?" Dina wondered. "I suppose those light-hearted newlyweds just didn't think about calling ahead." But that didn't ease her anxiety. Dina so much wanted to impress her new sister-in-law, Bracha, whose mother was the perfect *balabusta*. Bracha had a spick-and-span upbringing and Dina didn't want her to think she had married into a sloppy family. If only she could find two clean matching cups, coffee, tea, sugar, a tray and oh, yes, let's not forget the cake. Then her heart began to flutter. Where was each item? Dina quickly washed the cups as she tried to remember. The sugar was the easiest to find because it was next to the cereal on the counter. She found the coffee in a bag of groceries stashed next to the pantry door. The tray was perched atop the *milchig* pots. But the tea — where did she leave it? She opened the top middle kitchen cabinet, the top left cabinet, the top right cabinet, bingo. A square, blue cardboard box peeked out of a corner next to the glass serving plate used for *sheva berachos*. With a feeling of triumph, she took out the delicious cookies that her sister Malki had sent yesterday and placed them on the tray. After a twenty-minute ordeal and, finally, some shouts of "Dina, Dina, where have you disappeared to?" she appeared with a smile and a tray of steaming hot drinks and cookies. "How lovely," Bracha said. "You are quite a *balabusta*." Dina winced. If she only knew!

This incident was the last straw. Dina knew she had to get organized.

"Dina, my friend, I am going to teach you a little trick that will change your life," I said during our consultation. "Establish 'centers.' "

"What are 'centers'?" she asked.

I explained that centers were storage areas for things commonly used together. You could organize, for example, baking centers, beverage centers, nosh centers, pasta centers, cleaning centers. In other words, store items that are used together in the same place. Set aside one shelf for all your baking equipment: appliances, bowls, measuring spoons, beaters, spatula, and so forth. Establish one shelf for those items you use when serving guests: coffee, tea, hot chocolate, sugar, saccharine, and so on. This may mean doubling up on sugar or other inexpensive food items which must be included in several centers. Assign one place for nosh, high up and away from the kids. Anything you use together, store together.

Now Dina amazes her unexpected company with delicious cookies (recipe care of Malki) and the alacrity with which they are served.

⊷ Question 4 — Tammy Didn't Ask It

Tammy lifted the new cookbooks out of the box and placed them on her yellow kitchen table. She had received them at her bridal shower. Now, three weeks after the wedding, she wondered where they should go? She turned around, surveying the sunny roc n. A windowsill caught her eye and she walked over to it. Yes, it was just the perfect size to hold all of the cookbooks. Happily, she aligned the books on the windowsill over her *milchig* sink.

This arrangement seemed ideal until the following Monday. As she removed *Classic Kosher Cooking*, the cookbook next to it fell into a pot of burned macaroni that had been soaking in the sink. "Oh, no!" Tammy panicked, "my mother-in-law will be devastated when she sees what has become of the cookbook she gave me." She dried it as thoroughly as possible but the damage was evident. Stashing the book in the bottom of the bedroom closet, she hoped no one would discover the unfortunate accident.

The next morning was dark and dreary, bringing with it a heavy rain. An hour before supper Tammy went into the kitchen to leaf through *Come Cook With Us*, a present from her friend Tzili, only to find that it was soaking wet. "Oh no! The rainwater leaked through the window!" Tammy cried out in horror. Quickly, she removed the five remaining cookbooks from the sill and placed them next to the radiator to dry. "What a fiasco. How could I have made such a mistake?" she wondered.

Called in to assess the damage, I answered her question with a question. "When you took the cookbooks out of the box did you ask, 'Where is the most appropriate place for these cookbooks in terms of their size and the material they are made of'?"

"No," she answered. "I saw the windowsill and thought that they would look nice there. Now I realize that it was a foolish place to keep them because they are easily damaged by water. From now on I will pay closer attention to where I organize my belongings. I never thought that the wrong location could literally invite an accident."

I glanced around the room and something caught my eye. "Look at that glass bowl on the shelf over your kitchen table," I said. "Do you think that is the best place for it in terms of this new rule?"

"Come to think of it, the bowl is too wide for the shelf and could easily fall and break. But that shelf would certainly be a good place for my cookbooks," she grinned and added, "when they dry out."

⋅§ Question 5 — Mimi Didn't Ask It

Mimi ran to the laundry room carrying bottles of floor cleaner and wax. Her children would be home from school any minute and she didn't want to forget to put away these dangerous chemicals before they returned. Shuddering, she remembered grabbing the bottle of wax from four-year-old Shmuley just as he was about to swallow its contents. After that incident she realized that cleaning fluids could not be stored under the kitchen sink. The safest place was on a high shelf in the laundry room.

However, this new arrangement was problematic. It took three times as long to put everything away after she finished cleaning; because the shelf was too high for her to reach, and she needed the ladder. Her husband's ladder had to be carried from the garage to the laundry room, then it had to be opened, and the climb up was slow and shaky. Usually time was short, so in the end she just plunked everything down on the washing machine. Periodically, throughout the day, she would remind herself to retrieve the ladder from the garage and put the cleaning fluids back.

During a consultation with Mimi, I noticed that her washing machine was cluttered. "Why don't you store your cleaning supplies on that empty shelf up there?" I asked innocently.

"Because it's too high for me to reach, and I didn't have a chance to get our ladder so that I could put everything away up there," she answered.

"Why do you make things so hard on yourself? When looking for storage space, don't forget to ask yourself question number five: Is it easy to put away? If it isn't easy, then make it easy. Either store the ladder in here. . ."

"No, I can't do that," she interrupted. "My husband needs it in the garage."

"Then keep a stool here next to the washing machine and whenever you want to use the shelf — presto — you can reach it in an instant," I said.

Mimi laughed, "Why didn't I think of that!"

❦ ❦ ❦

Once you ask yourself these five questions you will discover the ideal location for each of your belongings. Now it's time to consider prime space and the types of storage space available to house each item.

◌§ Prime Space

When organizing items for convenience it is important to consider *prime space*. Prime space refers to the area most accessible to you. It is usually defined as any storage space that is no lower than your knee and no higher than your forehead. This is the most convenient range for storing and retrieving objects. If something is stored higher or lower than this, it becomes uncomfortable for someone to bend down so low or simply impossible to stretch up so high to reach an item. Therefore, any storage area that is considered prime space should be reserved for those articles you use frequently.

The front and back of each shelf is given a number rating. This rating corresponds to how easy it is for you to reach that space.

Place 1 — easy to reach
Place 2 — stretch slightly or bend
Place 3 — stretch fully or bend
Place 4 — stand on tip toes or stool
Place 5 — stand on a stool

The following diagram will illustrate this concept in detail.

This is only an example. When you look at your own shelves give them each a number rating according to how easy or difficult it is for you to reach that area.

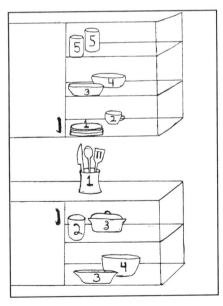

After you give the front and back of each shelf a number, take each item off of the shelf and evaluate it. Give each one a number rating as follows:

Item 1 — used a few times a day or once a day
Item 2 — used once a week or less
Item 3 — used once a month or less
Item 4 — used bimonthly or less
Item 5 — rarely used but I want to keep it

Match each item with its place: put item 1 in place 1, item 2 in place 2, and so on. Now you have found the perfect place to store each of your belongings.

◄§ Inch by Inch

There are two distinct types of storage: visible and concealed. Examples of visible storage units are open shelves, shelves with see-through doors, mug racks, hanging pot racks, coat trees, and the like. Examples of concealed storage units are: cabinets, drawers, chests, suitcases, boxes, and so forth. Because visible storage is usually open, it makes item retrieval simpler; concealed storage is less convenient because you must open a door, or pull out a drawer. In addition to convenience, appearance can also be taken into account. It must be noted that some items like books maintain a neat and organized appearance when stored visibly, while other items, like paperwork, are better stored concealed. A beautiful vase looks attractive on an open shelf; a bag of noodles doesn't. Neither visible nor concealed storage units are useful if they are disorganized. Yet each can be used to its best advantage if the following ideas are taken into consideration.

◄§ Visible Versus Concealed Storage

Baila's husband was a budding home carpenter. With no time to master the art of cabinet-making, he worked exclusively with shelves. Not only were they functional but they were economical too. Rather than buying kitchen cabinets, he put up shelves. Instead of acquiring a medicine cabinet, he installed a shelf. Instead of investing in a bookcase, he built shelves. The entire house was filled with wonderful, practical shelving. There was only one problem — the house looked like a second-hand store. At our meeting I pointed out to Baila, "Some things are meant to be displayed and other things, like your vacuum cleaner replacement bag, are not."

Before deciding whether to make use of shelves or cabinets, assess the items you are storing for: 1) decorative appeal; 2) protection and upkeep of item; 3) safety (from children); and 4) cost.

Visible storage space is ideal when displaying items that are both decorative and practical. If you own flower vases, ceramic coffee mugs, and attractive spice bottles, why not store them where they can be seen and easily reached? But if you have a small child who will take these items, then storing them in a concealed storage unit might be preferable. A glass breakfront cabinet in the living room highlights your heirloom silver candelabrum, kiddush cups and elegant serving pieces, as well as protecting them from dust and dirt.

Items used often, to which you need easy access, such as cooking utensils, can be hung on the kitchen wall or placed on the counter in an attractive container. Books look neat and organized on open shelves and generally don't need to be stored behind doors unless exposure to sunlight or water may cause damage.

In most cases, open storage units are also more economical than closed units. A coat rack is less expensive than a free-standing closet. A kitchen cabinet is costly; a hanging pot rack is not. Plastic or metal cabinet organizers are appropriate if you do not want to invest in any structural changes in your rented apartment.

In your garage, storage room and laundry room, accessibility is more important than aesthetics. A loop on the garage wall for hanging a hose or a rack of hooks for placing your broom, mop and other utensils are two examples. Laundry detergent, bleach, fabric softener, and similar supplies can be stored on a shelf above your washing machine — convenient for you, too high for small children.

In contrast, food products displayed on an open shelf will lend your kitchen a disorganized appearance. Nosh stored in a visible place will provide an open invitation to your children. Glasses, dishes and pots can be housed on an open shelf, but they will collect dust in addition to creating a feeling of clutter. Though your sewing box may appear attractive on the corner shelf, it could constitute a hazard for young children. Teddy bears, dolls, and figurines sit sweetly on a shelf, but the bulk of children's toys do not. (And by rotating toys and games, you ensure that they never lose their appeal.) Concealed storage — cabinets, drawers, chests, suitcases, boxes and so forth — provides the natural solution.

~§ Reorganizing Shelves, Drawers, Hooks and Racks

Chana had adequate storage space in each room of her apartment. Once a month she dutifully organized and arranged each shelf, drawer and closet. Why did the order disintegrate so quickly? She was always rummaging through the kitchen containers to find her spatula, while her pareve knife constantly disappeared into a "black hole." Her husband's socks had a will of their own, opposing all efforts to unite them. She was baffled. Why did her "organization" work against her? Like Chana, many women waste precious time reorganizing, when a proper under-standing of the best use of shelves, drawers, and hanging space would make this task unnecessary.

~§ Shelves

Narrow shelves are convenient for frequently used items, whereas deep shelves are highly impractical for everyday use. The interior is difficult to see and frustrating to reach. So keep your deep shelves in reserve for long-term storage (for example, six months).

Items that stand on their own (like books, plates, canned goods, boxed goods, stackable items and so forth) can be stored on shelves. Always keep in mind that shelves which are on view must maintain an orderly appearance. Assorted odds and ends will not add to the decor of your room.

Adjustable shelving, that is, shelves that rest on metal pins inserted in cabinet sides, or shelves resting on a track-and-clip system, are the most practical. Each shelf can be adjusted to suit your particular storage needs.

To maximize shelf space, a variety of practical solutions are available at home improvement centers. Shelf organizers for holding plates, cups, placemats, napkins, pans and pan lids can sometimes double your shelf space capacity.

⊸§ Drawers

Shallow drawers are convenient for small items and personal accessories. Wooden or plastic dividers, and small boxes or baskets will keep the drawers orderly. Bulkier items need deeper drawers. But remember that when the contents of drawers are stacked high and you can't find that Shabbos cardigan without pulling out all the sweaters on top of it, chaos often results. Therefore, it is important to assign each item to a specific drawer and to avoid stuffing too many items into each one.

⊸§ Hooks and Racks

You can free your cabinet shelving for priority items by using hooks and racks on the interior of the cabinet. They promote efficiency because items can be spotted at a glance. In addition, they increase storage space. Consider wall mounted racks for cooking utensils, pots, pans, and so forth, when kitchen cabinet space is limited.

৶ The Kosher Kitchen —
A Mitzvah Center

With a growing family and innumerable guests, Leah spent most of her day in the kitchen. She longed to redecorate it, to make it cheerful, homey and organized. Most important, she wanted to prevent mix-ups between *milchig* and *fleishig*. No book she had ever read had addressed this problem.

So she made a survey of neighborhood kitchens. One friend used individual storage units for her microwave, food processor, mixer and juicer. Even her sponges rested in built-in units under the sink. The kitchen was always neat and surgically clean. Another friend preferred open shelves, pots hanging from racks and a revolving spice rack on the counter. Everything was in order, but Leah knew that if it were her kitchen she wouldn't have the time or energy to keep it that way. She dragged herself home, her head pounding.

Still lacking a solution to her problem, Leah asked for my advice. Here is what I told her:

To keep a kosher kitchen, dairy, meat and pareve must be separate, but not so far apart that you feel like you're running in a marathon. (For that you would need your sneakers and they are at the bottom of a deep drawer!) In addition, your system must be simple enough to be maintained by older children or household help.

Barring the utopia of separate counters, sinks, cabinets, stovetops and ovens, there do exist satisfactory alternatives. Your stove can serve as the dividing line, *milchig* to your right, *fleishig* to your left. One counter or corner can be kept pareve, serving as a baking center. Your microwave and food processor can also be kept there. Or, if you have space, an island built in the middle of your kitchen can be the pareve baking center.

Who doesn't dream of a special Pesach kitchen? Although this is not feasible for everyone, you can certainly make life easier for yourself during that time of year by reorganizing. This "kitchen" doesn't have to be large. One cupboard in your present kitchen could be used for Pesach storage all year around. A creative, practical idea is a "roving cabinet," which can be stored in another room and wheeled into the kitchen when Pesach comes.

To prevent mix-ups of *milchig* and *fleishig*, pots, pans, dishes, silverware and containers of each should have completely different designs or colors. When your mixing bowls and other utensils look similar — especially if you are not the only one working in the kitchen — attach colored labels. Red for meat, blue for dairy and white or yellow for pareve are easy to remember. You may want to consider plates and cups with a blue design for *milchig* and red for *fleishig*; storage containers can echo the same motif. Bold colors don't appeal to you? Consider gold and silver instead. My personal system is to use round containers for *milchigs* and square containers for *fleishigs*.

๙ Kitchen Design

The kosher kitchen poses its own unique challenge with the divisions of milk, meat and pareve sections. Proper set-up and organization will help towards this aim. On the following page are five examples of common kitchen layouts. (These are not drawn to scale and are not accurate for carpentry or architectural purposes.)

If you sometimes feel as if you are running around in circles as you work in the kitchen, it could be that you really are. Frequent use of small kitchen appliances (food processor, mixer, toaster oven) keeps you hopping if they must constantly be moved from cabinet to working space and back again. If counter space is adequate, on-counter storage provides a great timesaver. And it need not be unsightly. Appliances can be stored in the furthest corner of the counter, in a "garage." This

1. This layout is usually found in the small apartments young couples rent. It has only one sink, which requires separate inserts for dish washing. Assign one counter next to the sink for meat and the other side for dairy. Use the counter in between the fridge and oven for a pareve baking and/or appliance center. Place a large meat or dairy cutting board on the pareve section when you require more work space, (or, if the counters are *treife*). Divide meat and dairy sections by designating the top cupboards for your meat utensils and the bottom for your dairy utensils or assign the upper and lower cupboards left of the sink for your meat utensils and the upper and lower cupboards right of the sink for your dairy utensils. Store meat and dairy silverware in separate drawers in their respective sections of the kitchen to avoid mix-ups.

2. This layout has all of the cupboards and sinks on one wall in a straight line. If possible, build a marble or plastic partition between the two sinks thereby creating a division between the dairy and meat sinks. Designate the upper cabinets above the dairy sink for dairy utensils. Designate the upper cabinets above the meat sink for meat utensils. If possible, pareve items should be assigned to a cabinet in between the dairy and meat sections to allow easy access from both areas.

If there is room, a small dinette and refrigerator can be placed against the opposite wall. If the stove and oven are next to one counter, for example, the meat one, then place a large cutting board with your dairy utensils on the counter next to the stove when cooking dairy. This will help prevent you from accidentally placing hot dairy food on your meat counter. It will also prevent you from grabbing a meat spoon to stir the contents of the dairy pot.

3. All of the cupboards are in a straight line against one wall with the stove and oven in the middle dividing the two sinks. The stove acts as a natural divider between the milk and meat sections of the kitchen. The refrigerator and dinette are next to the other wall. If the kitchen is large enough you can have a small pareve baking center on the other wall or a small Pesach cupboard.

4. This layout features meat and dairy sections on two separate walls. This plan is practical for a small narrow kitchen or a very large kitchen. It keeps your meat and dairy sections completely separate. You have the option of installing a dishwasher and stovetop in each section, if you so desire. Depending on the size and layout of the room you might decide to build an additional cupboard on the third wall or install an island between the counters for your pareve baking needs. The island can have a built-in stovetop.

5. This layout has the cupboards on two perpendicular walls. Designate one wall for meat and the other for dairy. If the kitchen is large enough you may prefer installing separate stoves and dishwashers in each section. An island in the center of the room is another possibility. Consider setting aside one cabinet for storing Pesach utensils.

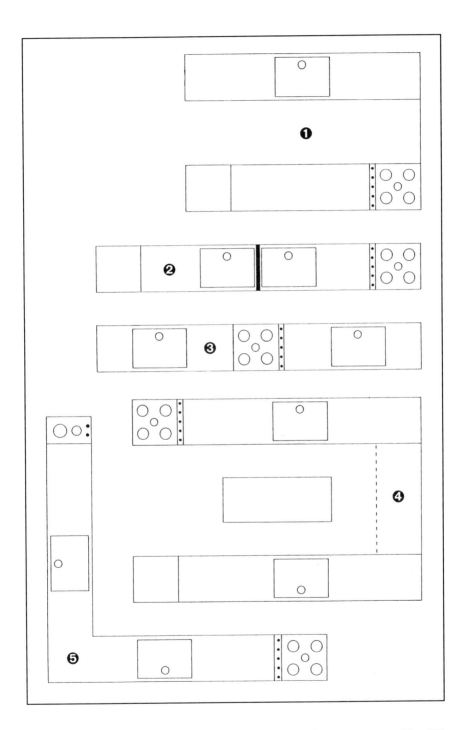

cabinet, which rests on the counter, has a roll-up tambour door or swing-out doors. If counter space is minimal, consider a swing-up shelf or a deep drawer built into your bottom cabinet, directly under the counter. If the drawer is fitted with a sliding lid, it can double as a surface on which to place your food processor or mixer when in use.

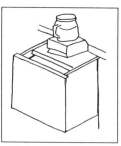

A lift-out shelf for mixer. Drawer underneath stores additional mixer parts.

A sliding lid serves as a work surface for an appliance. To store appliance, simply slide lid back and put item into the deep drawer.

Tambour door rolls up to reveal appliances.

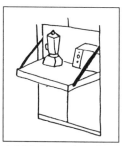
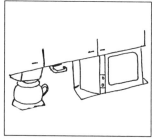

Bi-fold doors open and close easily for easy access to your appliances.

A fold-down door for appliances doubles as a work surface.

Cabinet mounted appliances.

Breakable bottles (grape juice, wine, soda, and so forth) present a particular challenge. Pull-out wire racks built into bottom cabinets are most efficient for storage. They have a large capacity, and all contents are clearly visible. A deep dishpan placed on a lower cabinet shelf can serve the same purpose. Bottles can also be stored in deep drawers with drawer inserts or on shallow shelves which offer easy access. Wine and grape juice bottles can be stored horizontally on notched wooden strips placed on lower cabinet shelves or on shelves mounted on the wall.

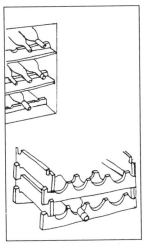  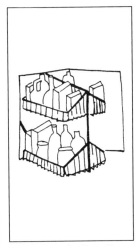

Stacking racks for bottles keeps each one accessible.

Bottle drawers and drawer inserts will keep your bottles organized.

Pull-out racks for efficient storage of bottles and other containers.

There are also a number of commercially marketed wine racks available in metal or wood which can be placed in your kitchen, dining room or wherever you please.

Canned and boxed goods are commonly stored in upper cabinets, but it takes only one person in a rush to turn order into chaos. More efficient are pull-out wire baskets, drawers or narrow shelves. If you must use deep shelves, store doubles directly behind the item in use. This serves as an immediate reminder that it is time to restock your supply.

For fast cleanups, cleaning supplies should be stored where you need them most. Keep spray bottles, rags, sponges and paper towels or Handiwipes in a basket in the kitchen and in every bathroom, facilitating quick, easy and hassle-free cleaning.

Dishes are usually stacked in upper cabinets. When convenient, they can also be stored in deep drawers or upright, in a plate rack on a shelf or on a counter.

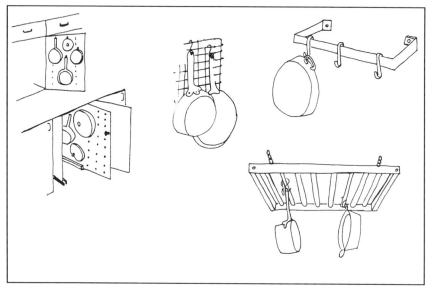

Pot and pan storage ideas for easy retrieval.

Store pots and pans in oversized drawers, on vertical pegboard pull-outs, on wall-mounted pot racks, or on hanging pot racks suspended from the ceiling.

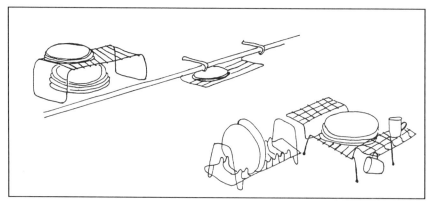

Extend the storage capacity of your shelves with these products.

Much footwork is eliminated when spices are housed in portable spice racks or on a lazy Susan. Individual bottles can be brought to any counter or table when needed, and easily put back without misplacing them.

Trash can be stored in a pedal-operated wastebasket, in a standard rubber trash can, under the sink in a pull-out bin, in a tilt-out compartment, or mounted on the door under the sink.

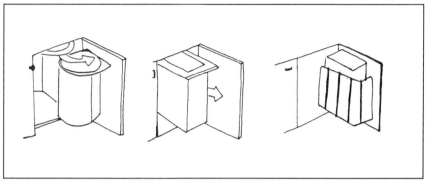

Choose a trash container to suit your needs.

Kitchen towels can be kept under the sink on a rack attached to the door, under upper cabinets directly above the counter, on a wall rack or hook next to the sink, or on the side of a lower cabinet.

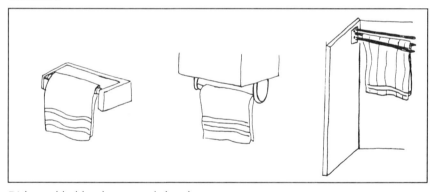

Dishtowel holders keep towels handy.

✍ Goodbye Clutter

This mischief maker is the number one archenemy of organization, permeating the home, the mind and the spirit, and bogging you down. More persistent than your three year old and trickier than a fox, this culprit enlists everyone's help, including

your friends and relatives. Working with the support of senti-
ment, this troublemaker is a more bothersome pest than a
cockroach and just as difficult to get rid of. No, he is not your
two-year-old son. The enemy is CLUTTER.

Yes, clutter is the reason you can't find what you need when
you need it. One of the most basic steps to reorganization is
getting rid of clutter and keeping it out. We know this is a job for
the very brave and persistent. With a battle plan, the appropriate
weapons, and determination you should succeed in the war
against clutter.

To start you need:

    1. 10 medium sized boxes
    2. 1 file box with a package of file cards or a notebook
    3. 3 large trash bags
    4. a package of smaller, transparent plastic bags
    5. a package of folders and an expanding folder
    6. 1 black marker

Don't ask questions yet; just assemble the above and then we
can begin.

Good, now that you've gathered the boxes and bags, I will
explain the operation. The three large trash bags facilitate
"de-junking." Label one bag: Throw Away (it should be large).
Label a second bag: Give Away. Label the
third bag: Put Away. The smaller package of
clear plastic bags is used for organizing the
Put Away and Give Away bags. For example,
suppose you want to give away two dresses to
your sister and a few pairs of children's shoes
to a local *chesed* orga-
nization. Place the
dresses in one bag and
the shoes in another,
mark each bag, then
place both in the larger
plastic bag labeled
"Give Away."

One of clutter's most ingenious tricks is to get you so befuddled that you storm a room and empty all the closets at once. While your adrenalin is still flowing you gleefully trash most items in sight. You gain a sense of accomplishment, but then you begin to tire. As time runs out, you stuff the remnants of your assault back into the closet — or worse yet, you leave it on the floor and promise yourself that you will come back later. Again clutter has defeated you.

But not this time, for you have a battle plan.

Choose the one room which is absolutely the most cluttered. Then, select the closet or corner that irritates you the most. Zero in on the messiest shelf or spot and that is where we will begin today.

Before you shove the contents out with glee, stop. Gently push everything to one side, taking out only one item at a time. Or if there is no space, then remove the contents of one shelf only, not the entire closet. Now examine each object, asking yourself: When was the last time I used this? If you haven't used it for a long time ask yourself: Would it matter if I gave it away? Consider giving it away if you won't need it but someone else will. If you aren't sure whether to keep an item or to give it away, follow this rule: If it is expensive or not easily replaceable, hold on to it; if not, give it away. If the item is broken and neither you nor anyone else can use it, then throw it out (in the labeled bag). Don't feel badly about it — after all, everything has a limited life span. Look at it this way: Would you feel sad if you lost five pounds? Chances are you wouldn't choose to hold onto those pounds just because you've had them for so long or because your Aunt Minnie gave them to you.

If you do use the item, ask yourself: Is this the right space for it? If the answer is yes, return it to the cabinet; if no, place it in the bag labeled "Put Away."

The package of folders and the expanding folder will hold miscellaneous papers. Designate a folder for different categories, such as documents, medical papers, bills, warranties and guarantees, and so on, and put each folder in a separate pocket of the expanding folder. When you come across mislaid papers, simply file them in the appropriate folders.

To reorganize the cabinet or shelf once you've eliminated the clutter, turn to page 69 to view the organization chart. Remember to resist the urge to pack too much into the shelf. In this case, less is more.

After going through one room, you will have three bags. Throw out the "Throw Away" bag. Make arrangements for the "Give Away" bag to be distributed or put it in a closet and add more give away items as you continue de-cluttering. Then you will be left with a "Put Away" bag. When you evaluate the items in the "Put Away" bag ask yourself: Why is it in this cabinet in the first place? The answer will be one of the following:

　1. Because it is most needed in this area

2. Because I don't return items to their proper location — I just dump them in the first empty space I see
3. Because its assigned place is too inconvenient
4. Because I don't have a place for it

Once you've identified the reason for storing the item there, you can now find a more suitable location for it.

Put away the more frequently used items using the rules on page 86 (at a glance #2). Now you will be left with items that you use on an infrequent basis or don't need at this particular time, such as: fabric scraps, off-season clothing, clothing that doesn't fit (clothing that is too small, maternity clothing, or clothing you're keeping for a new baby) old school notebooks, and the like. These items should be stored in boxes and placed in a basement, attic, storage room, or other unused storage space. Before you store the boxes, label each box with a number and a brief description of its contents, then record on the file card or in the notebook the number, contents and location of the box. For example: 1. Boys' winter clothing, ages 10-12, on lower shelf in basement.

Toys can be separated into boxes, too. Shabbos toys can be placed in a box and left in a cabinet, then taken out on Friday evening. Other boxes can be used to store toys for rainy days or special occasions such as birthdays.

As you de-clutter you will feel lighter, as if you've lost fifteen pounds. And you have. All of those items took up living space and mental space. You will no longer have to think about all those extra items, what to do with them or how to shift them back and forth between closets.

Don't be fooled into stopping after one de-cluttering session. Aim for one half-hour session three times a week, or an hour-and-a-half session once a week. Keep going until you've de-cluttered your entire house. In other words, stay on the offensive.

Now it's time to discuss the defense. Don't ever let clutter enter your house again. It will try to creep back in the form of unusable gifts from Cousin Selma, treasures from your old friend Rivka which were cluttering her house until she read this book, junk mail, and all other printed matter you don't remember bringing into the house. Don't let down your guard now that you've come this far. Get rid of this stuff BEFORE it makes itself comfortable in your living room. Establish a regular time to purge all rooms of paperwork and reading material that is no longer current.

Once you have done this you will know the battle is over. You have won the war.

STEP FOUR — AT A GLANCE

1. Store items in convenient locations.

2. Follow the five storage rules: a) store item where it is used; b) store frequently used items in easy to reach locations; c) store items used together in the same location; d) store fragile or unusual shaped items in places best suited to them; e) make it easy to store and retrieve item.

3. Use prime space for frequently used items. Use non-prime space for infrequently used items.

4. Store decorative or neat looking items in visible storage units such as shelves. Store paperwork or messy looking items in concealed storage units such as drawers and cabinets.

5. Use shelves for items that are easy to stack. Use drawers for hard to stack items.

6. Don't overstuff shelves or drawers

7. Keep *milchig* and *fleishig* completely separate; choose utensils having distinctly different designs or colors, and store in separate drawers or cabinets.

8. To conquer clutter, set aside a regular time to de-junk. Attack most offensive shelf first and go through each item one at a time to determine whether it should be: thrown out, stored in a different location, returned to same location.

Step Five
Meal Management

This section will help you develop your own meal management system. It will discuss how to make the most of your food preparation time, and keep menus varied. It will offer suggestions on the best use of your freezer and will revolutionize your Shabbos cooking.

When I was single I never understood why the conversation of a group of intelligent Jewish homemakers always degenerated into the exchange of cooking hints and favorite recipes. What transformed bright women into kitchen kooks? I couldn't figure it out. Then I got married. When I joined the ranks of newlyweds I was shocked and overwhelmed by shopping, and planning and preparing meals each and every day of the week, including Shabbos. I never realized how much people eat. Whenever I was certain that I had made a lot there wasn't enough; whenever I thought I had made too little, there were leftovers from Sunday until Thursday. Whenever I was sure that I had allotted enough time for cooking, I found I had not accounted for the time required to wash and cut vegetables, clean chickens or check for insects. I panicked when a new recipe entailing hours of work was inedible. Worst of all, I saw myself becoming enslaved to my kitchen, joining those masses of women searching for the perfect recipe. I was determined to get out of this mess before the complaints began that I never made spaghetti like Adina's mommy did.

◄§ Weekday Cooking

Like most women I knew, I realized that I approached cooking as I handled housework. I understood that it had to be done everyday, but wished it would miraculously disappear. Mine was a haphazard approach, one day gourmet, the next day store-bought pizza. Either I didn't have time to make what I really wanted to make or I had just run out of the required ingredients.

I realized that I needed to schedule cooking and preparation time. (Preparation includes checking for bugs, cleaning vegetables, and so on.) Planning ahead would eliminate the problems of being caught in the middle of cooking without the necessary ingredients, or serving dinner an hour late. Moreover, scheduling is essential for Shabbos preparation or any special occasion. It eliminates the need for making zero-hour decisions along with the subsequent tensions this creates, and it allows for a smooth transition from preparation to cooking to serving.

In order to schedule cooking time, all factors must be taken into consideration: your work schedule, your children's schedule, the baby's feeding schedule, and the like. For example, if you work three mornings a week, cooking should be scheduled for the mornings that you are home. Prepare enough for the three days when your schedule is tight and cooking is most difficult.

Here are three more scheduling possibilities:

1. Cook Every Day

This suits someone whose main objective is to serve fresh food. This can be accomplished even by someone working full-time if she uses a menu plan tailored to her needs: fast and easy to prepare.

2. Cook Double

The additional portions are used the next day or frozen for a future meal. Thus, large blocks of time are created to run errands, accomplish other household tasks, or have time for yourself on those special days when the meal is prepared in advance.

3. Cook Once a Week

This system works especially well for women who work full-time or have many "extracurricular" activities. The advantage of this system is that since all the meals are prepared during a large block of time one day a week, you are free from having to cook the rest of the week.

Each of these systems has its unique advantages and disadvantages. One may be appropriate for you at one point in your life; variations may be necessary periodically. What's important is that you create a system that works *for* you, not *against* you. Remember, a meal management system can help you only if it suits your schedule and cooking style.

A successful system contains four elements:

1. food list
2. menu plan
3. properly organized recipes
4. shopping list

Each of these elements is useful in and of itself, so if the entire system seems too complicated, then use the part appropriate for your needs. It can only increase your efficiency. You may want to start with one item, adding the rest as you become more organized. Or, you might implement all four and discover that one of them is unnecessary for your needs. The important thing is that you create a system which works for you. One indication that the system works, is if you adapt to it quickly.

The first time my friend Ora saw my food list attached to my refrigerator door she was very amused. I asked her if she had a better suggestion. After she described her methods, it became clear that she did in her head what I do on paper. She has a specific repetoire of meals and she makes them in a particular sequence. As you become more familiar with the system, this may happen to you as well.

1. The Food List

This is a list of the foods your family enjoys and which can be prepared often. It is divided into sections — *milchig, fleishig,* soups, salad, and so forth — with only the names of the recipes included in each section. The purpose of this list is to facilitate quick choices in planning a menu. It ensures variety, reminding you of your many options. Additions to the list are always welcome. If you have not already compiled a food list, then attach a piece of paper to the inside of a cupboard and start now. During one week, jot down all the meals you make that the family enjoys — that's all there is to it.

(For a sample food list, see Appendix A. Your list may be smaller or larger, one piece of paper or ten.)

2. The Menu Plan

Part two of a successful meal planning system is a menu plan. Even if this part is the only one implemented, you will have improved your system by seventy-five percent. A menu plan includes the names of every dish you will make for breakfast, lunch and dinner for a week or a month.

A written plan lets you and your family know which foods to buy, what to prepare and when. Thus, it enables other members of the family to help with meal preparation. A well-thought-out menu saves time and money, since planning allows you to adjust your meals, buying according to seasonal items. It prevents your experiencing that sinking feeling as you try to decide what to make for lunch minutes before your troops walk in through the door. And how often have you found yourself in the middle of a recipe when you realize that you are missing the major ingredient? A menu plan can avert this disaster. It also enables you to achieve variety, preventing you from serving the same meal on three consecutive days. But most importantly, a menu plan lets you cash in on accrued benefits.

Accrued benefits are extra benefits — two for the price of one, so to speak. Take just a few extra minutes while preparing your quiche for tonight's meal, to put together a second one. This one will be Tuesday's dinner, leaving time on Tuesday afternoon free for you. After all, you already have everything on hand and the mess has already been made. While the quiches are baking, the dishes can be washed, affording you the opportunity to leave the kitchen earlier than expected. With hardly more effort you can add a few vegetables to the ones you're already scrubbing, peeling and cutting for tonight's salad; tomorrow's sauteed vegetables are on their way.

However, in order to achieve these accrued benefits you must schedule cooking time and plan ahead in order to have the necessary ingredients on hand and to eliminate, or at least minimize distractions that can prevent you from finishing the job at hand. To reach this goal a menu plan should be drawn up.

To prepare a menu plan:

1. Take out your food list.
2. Keep season and budget in mind. (Is it too hot for chicken soup? Is squash available for a squash bake? Are tomatoes overpriced this week?)
3. Write down the meals for the week, including Shabbos.
4. Mark down ingredients needed.

The whole process usually takes fifteen minutes. It is worthwhile to plan at least one week at a time. If you want to delegate food preparation to other members of the family post up the plan in a convenient place with the name of each person written next to his assigned task. Thus, preparations can be started even when you are delayed unexpectedly. For sample menu plans based on the different cooking systems, see Appendix B.

3. Properly Organized Recipes

Part three of the system calls for properly organized recipes. For three-and-a-half years I copied and clipped recipes, throwing them into one drawer. I considered this an organized recipe system; every time I needed a recipe I plowed through that drawer. One day while visiting my friend, Bina, a super-*balabusta*, I noticed all of her recipes neatly arranged in a notebook, each page protected with plastic. Eureka!

Your recipe file should include recipes you consider successful, arranged according to categories in either a notebook, a photograph album or a file box. A separate section can be allotted to untried recipes. If you have recipes from cookbooks, you can note them in your personal recipe file by jotting down the names of the recipes and the page numbers of the cookbook on which the entire recipe can be found. When using a cookbook, put a star next to the recipe name in the cookbook index, or compile a list of the recipes that interest you on the inside cover of the cookbook. After trying a new recipe, make a note next to it indicating success or failure and your own ideas for improvement such as baking time, pan size, and so forth.

Organizing your recipes saves time and effort when you are under pressure. It also prevents your experimenting with the same recipe twice, only to discover once again that it is a flop or, your family doesn't like it.

4. The Shopping List

A shopping list is the most effective reminder of the items you need to buy. The list, together with a pen, must be kept in an accessible place. As soon as you are running low on an item, mark it on your shopping list. Don't wait until you have run out of the product completely. Shopping lists can be organized according to store section if you shop in one supermarket (dairy, produce, frozen goods, canned goods), or according to the stores you shop in (butcher shop, bakery, kosher market, pharmacy, and so forth).

Thus you have the basis for creating or improving your own meal planning system.

Where there is the most potential for *kedushah* and growth, Satan fights the hardest and puts in his strongest efforts. One of the Satan's tricks is to belittle the importance of our actions in our own eyes, so that we will not do the job properly. It is unfortunate that he has succeeded in convincing society at large that our role as a yiddishe mother is not glorious. One of the areas where this is particularly noticeable is in our attitude towards cooking healthy meals for our families.

One of the loftiest ideals a Jew strives for is to emulate the ways of Hashem. In blessing Him after we eat, we say *hazon es haolam* (Who feeds all the world). We praise Hashem for His kindness in providing food for every living creature. When a woman provides food for her family, taking into account their special needs, she is truly emulating the ways of Hashem. Upon realizing this, our meal preparation will now take on great importance and provide us with the satisfaction we need to carry us through every day.

⤳ In Honor of Shabbos

Many women enjoy Shabbos and Yom Tov cooking, while other women are overwhelmed each Shabbos and Yom Tov. Sit back for a moment and refocus your viewing lens. Zoom-in on the herculean task you are repeatedly accomplishing when you prepare for Shabbos. The amount of time required alone is mind-boggling. And what is actually being asked of you? Each *erev Shabbos* and *erev Yom Tov* you must meet a binding deadline. You must present two to three gourmet feasts which are expected to accommodate your family's preferences and dietary needs. Your ingenuity is continually put to the test in devising menus which conform to all halachic requirements. Ever heard of a French gourmet using a *blech*? Just La Yiddishe Mama. The difficulty of simmering a cholent overnight should not be under-estimated. Pesach potato cake anyone? Ask the non-*gebruchts* cook. She'll ply you with goodies that defy the laws of gravity.

You are the sole designer of all the culinary delights which enhance the Shabbos and Yom Tov table. However, even the most inspired homemaker must come to terms with her wily opponent — time. On those rare occasions when you have generous time slots, go ahead and *patchke*. Cook extra and freeze. But if you possess a total of two-and-a-half hours to complete your Shabbos cooking, consider buying challah, fish, and cake. Prepare simple meals. If you have a newborn and several young children, you might want to buy certain foods on a regular basis.

When family members are ill, convalescing or in need of exten-sive care, you might consider hiring a cook. This suggestion might sound outrageous at first, but it is well worth it. During my first pregnancy I was bedridden for three months. My husband and I quickly tired of store-bought foods and the doctor disap-proved of the high sugar and salt content. We hired Batsheva — the gourmet *tzaddekes* — who came in once a week, straining our budget much less than cleaning help would have (my husband managed the cleaning, and paper plates solved the dirty dish dilemma). Batsheva not only cooked well, but she also revealed many tricks of her trade, and we found it difficult to part with her even after our child was born.

But since a cook is not always practical, it's worthwhile to have an emergency stock in the freezer which will assure your Shabbos joy, despite the inevitable, unpredictable crises. Here are also a few suggestions for quick Shabbos meals when you find yourself in dire straits:

⋖§ Emergency Shabbos Menus

1. One pot — Chicken, potatoes, carrots, onion and water (enough for soup).

   The soup is eaten with soup nuts. The vegetables and chicken constitute the main meal. The remaining chicken, potatoes and carrots with small amount of soup becomes cholent for Shabbos day.

2. Two pots — In one pot put chicken soup. In second pot put same ingredients as chicken soup with less water and leave overnight on *blech* for cholent.

3. Roast meat and potatoes with frozen vegetables all served hot Friday night. For lunch serve roast cold. Add mayonnaise and vegetables to potatoes for potato salad.

4. Broiled chicken or roast and cholent. Serve potatoes from cholent and broiled chicken on Friday night. Serve cholent and cold broiled chicken on Shabbos day.

⋙ Cooking Efficiently

Whether you are planning an elaborate Shabbos, Yom Tov, or *sheva berachos* menu, success depends on how well you schedule each task. Before you can create a schedule however, you must be aware of exactly how much time is required to prepare each item. How long does it *really* take to peel ten cucumbers for a salad, or to clean your chicken, or to put together the batter for your cake?

❅ ❅ ❅

The following are two sample Shabbos menus employing different, yet efficient, meal-management methods. Choose the one which seems most suited to your cooking style:

Shabbos Menu A:
(For women who cook in the mornings)

Friday Night:
Tuna salad, carrot salad, chicken soup with noodles, baked chicken and potatoes, green beans, cake

Shabbos day:
borekas, cucumber salad, cholent, cold baked chicken, schnitzel, cake

Third meal:

tuna salad, egg salad, carrot salad, cucumber salad, quiche

Wednesday: Preparation to be done in the afternoon or evening.

1. Check lettuce.

2. Check rice and barley for cholent (if necessary).

3. Bake double cake recipe (freeze one).

4. While cake is baking, wash all pots, pans and dishes. (Tomorrow is Thursday so sink and counter space must be clean.)

5. Prepare sandwiches for Thursday.

6. Freeze cake.

Thursday: Everyone in school. Each minute precious.

(All times are approximate — you might work faster or slower than indicated here.)

9:00 Boil eggs, green beans, noodles.

(Either leave dishes to soak or wash as you go.)

9:15 Clean chickens and cut up.

9:45 Separate chicken, half in soup pot, marinate the rest and refrigerate.

Pareve next. Wash hands well.

9:55 Take out pareve knife, cutting board, vegetables and food processor.

Scrub or peel and then cut up vegetables for soup and quiche. Add half to soup and put on stove to cook. Put the rest of the vegetables in bowl for quiche.

10:05 Peel potatoes, cucumbers and carrots.

10:30 Grate carrots and slice everything else.

Put on respective dressings.

Put potatoes for cholent and Friday night chicken in bowl of water. Refrigerate potatoes and salads.

Cut vegetables into small pieces for tuna salad and vegetable borekas.

11:30 Make tuna salad and egg salad.

Refrigerate salads and green beans.

Clean up.

Make quiche and bake. Take soup off of stove.

12:00 Roll out borekas and fill.

12:30 Clean up.

Friday Morning:

8:30 Slice potatoes. Add oil and salt. Bake with chicken.

8:45 Bake borekas. Fry schnitzel (a double recipe).

9:30 Take borekas out.

Prepare cholent.

10:00 Wash dishes

10:30 Take chicken out of oven.

Clean house.

Shabbos Menu B:

(For women who cook in the evening)

Friday Night:

gefilte fish, carrot salad, chicken soup, chicken, fried zucchini, potato kugel, cake

Shabbos day:

gefilte fish, cucumber salad, sweet carrot tzimmes, cholent, cake

Third Meal:

tuna salad, potato or macaroni salad, cucumber salad, carrot salad

Thursday morning (before work):

Take out chicken and fish (if frozen) to defrost.

Thursday night:

7:00 Place on stove two large pots (for soup and cholent) and two small ones (for vegetable side dishes).

☐ Place on counter onions, potatoes, carrots, zucchini, celery, cucumbers and any other vegetables needed for cooking.

☐ Peel seven onions, add whole one to large pot with water. Turn on to boil. (This will be the soup.)

☐ Chop two onions and add to second large pot with oil, frying on low heat (for the cholent).

☐ Chop a fourth onion and put in one small pot (for the zucchini side dish).

- □ Meanwhile, peel and chop potatoes, adding to large pots (for cholent and soup).
- □ Clean chicken. Add wings and neck to soup, breasts and drumsticks to cholent. Add water to cholent.
- □ Peel and slice all but three carrots.
- □ Add sliced carrots to soup, cholent, and the second small pot (for tzimmes).
- □ Cook tzimmes on low heat.
- □ Peel and slice zucchini.
- □ Add to soup, cholent.
- □ Add the rest to pot containing chopped onion (for zucchini side dish).
- □ Begin cooking zucchini dish.
- □ Slice celery. Add to soup, cholent and zucchini.
- □ Grate potatoes. Put in bowl A (to be made into kugel).
- □ Grate two onions. Put one in bowl A. Put second in bowl B (for gefilte fish).
- □ Add ingredients from your favorite recipe to kugel (bowl A), transfer to baking pan and bake.
- □ The cholent, soup, two vegetable side dishes and kugel are cooking!

8:30 Prepare sauce, spices or batter and pour over chicken pieces. Either bake now or wait until kugel is finished.
- □ Grate remaining carrots. Add some to gefilte fish bowl. Put the rest in salad container (for carrot salad). Add dressing to carrot salad and refrigerate.
- □ Slice cucumbers and last onion. Place in container for cucumber salad. Add vinegar, oil, sugar and salt. Shake and place in fridge.

9:00 Take kugel out of oven and put chicken in.
- □ Remove tzimmes, zucchini, cholent and soup from stove.
- □ Wash hands well.
- □ Boil two pots of water on stove, one large, one small.
- □ Add peeled potatoes (or macaroni) to small pot (for potato or macaroni salad).

□ Add ground fish to bowl with grated onion and carrot. Add remaining ingredients. Mix, form into balls and add to large pot of boiling water.

9:45 Wash dishes.

10:30 Turn off fish and let cool.

□ Take out chicken

□ Put pots in fridge.

10:45 Go to bed. You've earned a good night's sleep.

Alternative (if you're too tired):

At 9:15, refrigerate prepared fish mixture and cook on Friday. Leave potato (or macaroni) salad and washing up for Friday while fish is cooking.

On Friday afternoon make tuna salad for lunch and for third meal.

⋲§ Shabbos Meals on the Blech

Most of us prepare traditional Shabbos foods such as chicken soup, cholent and gefilte fish. These foods are popular not only because they are tasty but also because they fit the halachic requirements of Shabbos. Gefilte fish eliminates the problem of *borer*, kugel is a *davar yavesh* and therefore can be heated on top of an inverted pot on the *blech*, and cholent tastes better the longer it is cooked. But what do you do if your children refuse to touch cholent, your husband doesn't like the standard potato kugel, you don't have time to *patchke* with gefilte fish and your guest is a vegetarian? Here are some suggestions for more unusual Shabbos meals either heated on the *blech* or cooked in a crock pot.

1. Spaghetti and meatballs: Cook meatballs and put in crock pot. Heat up cooked spaghetti in pan and put on top of hot water urn or on inverted pot on *blech.*

2. Shepherd's pie: Layer mashed potatoes and baked ground meat. Put on *blech.*

3. Potato kugel with meat: Add small pieces of cholent meat to potato kugel recipe and place in lightly greased crock pot. Leave until Shabbos lunch.

4. Mashed potatoes and schnitzel: Put mashed potatoes and schnitzel in flat pan and place on top of inverted pot on *blech.*

5. Borekas: Keep warm on top of pot resting on *blech.*

6. Meatloaf or hamburgers

7. Quiche or vegetable pie: Try squash, corn, broccoli or spinach.

8. Kugel: Instead of potatoes use rice, carrots, zuchini, or sweet noodle with apple or pineapple.

9. Fried or baked fish

Shopping Tips

When I think of shopping I'm reminded of a Yiddish joke:

There was a poor couple who saved their wages and twice a year went on a special shopping trip. The time came for one of their biannual expeditions and the wife was sick, so the husband went alone. His wife eagerly awaited his return, thinking about what her husband was buying — maybe a new dress for Yom Tov, maybe a new hat for himself. Finally her husband returned with two baby elephants. The wife was shocked and enraged. Of what use were a pair of elephants? Where would they keep them? Had her husband gone mad? But he explained, "They were two for the price of one. How could I pass up such a bargain?"

Many times we shop in the same way. We travel miles out of our way for a "bargain" without taking into consideration the time it takes or the extra gas we use and we end up buying items we do not need or even like, simply because they were on sale.

Some women love to go shopping. They enjoy clothes shopping, shoe shopping, grocery shopping and consider it the highlight of their day. Yet there are many women who dread shopping. Whether you're included in the former or latter category, shopping is an inescapable part of your life. Your time, budget, attitude, along with other factors, will all affect the way you shop. The following questions can help you prioritize your shopping needs and weigh your gains against your losses in time and money.

Where do you shop?

Do you shop in a store nearby?

Do they stock the items and *hechsherim* that you use?

Are you satisfied with the quality of the goods?

Are the prices standard?

Can you make an order by phone and have it delivered? Do you have to pay extra for delivery?

How often do you buy perishables: bread, milk, fruit and vegetables?

How often do you buy non-perishables: like laundry detergent, soap and shampoo?

How much storage space do you have?

Would you rather save time by shopping less often or save storage space by shopping more often? (Some items must be bought once a week; others can be bought once a year and kept in storage. Non-perishables such as soap, shampoo and laundry detergent are items that can be stored for long periods of time.)

Do you often run out of items?

Do you have a shopping list which is close at hand when you need it?

Do you mark down items as you run low?

When you're shopping, do you ask yourself: Is this item really necessary? Is there a cheaper equivalent I could use?

What is the more decisive factor — convenience or budget?

What is the store's payment policy?

Must you pay cash or can you charge?

The answers to these questions will help you clarify your priorities so that you can make your shopping time count and your money work for you.

⮑ The Freezer — A Balabusta's Best Friend

I will never forget the first time I met my Russian relatives. After years of aborted attempts to leave the Soviet Union they finally secured exit papers and arrived in *Eretz Yisrael.* We sat around our dining room table talking and exchanging information about the past years. There were so many things they wanted to know about my family. Then came a crucial question. There was a pause as the mother of the family studied my face carefully. "Is it true that in America everyone eats food from the freezer?" she asked me. Noting my blank expression she continued. "In Russia we heard that Americans stock only frozen food," she said. "Did you ever eat fresh food in your house?"

Although you certainly wouldn't want to eat frozen food every day, the freezer is one of the most useful organizational tools at your disposal. You can use your freezer to store meals for those days when there is no time to cook supper, or to keep in reserve side dishes and desserts for those Shabbosim for which you lacked sufficient time to prepare elaborate meals. It enables you to smile and say, "No problem," when two friends phone two hours before Shabbos and ask if they can stay at your house. When Tanta Esther shows up unexpectedly, your freezer will stand by your side. That yeast cake can be popped into the oven to warm in a few minutes, and your reputation as a *balabusta* will be saved. The freezer enables you to send a *lukshen* kugel to the neighbor with a new baby. Countless unnecessary trips to the store can also be eliminated through efficient freezer use.

To sum up, there are six good reasons to use your freezer. Your freezer will help you to:
1. Cut down on waste by freezing leftovers
2. Save money and effort by stocking up on sale items
3. Save cooking and shopping time
4. Enjoy cooking because you have less to do
5. Entertain without anxiety or exhaustion
6. Produce meals in a hurry

Your freezer can only be a friend to you if you treat it right. Judy, a client of mine, wanted to know what she had done wrong to deserve such unfair treatment from her freezer. Judy poured out her heart to me. She loved to cook and experiment with different recipes. Some were successful and some weren't; but even if they weren't, it didn't deter her from using them. If the meal wasn't eaten she put it in her freezer until. . . Judy also hated to throw out leftovers so she put them in her freezer until. . . Whenever Judy bought too much bread at the store she stuffed it in her freezer until. . .

Until Judy's husband was afraid to open the freezer door for fear of what would come flying out at him. But as far as he was concerned this was better than having to eat Judy's defrosted meals. He preferred toast with butter, noodles with tomato sauce, anything rather than those freezer leftovers. Judy wasn't using her freezer to its best advantage. I taught her how with the following ideas.

How *can* you use your freezer to its best advantage? It depends on your cooking style. If you don't want to cook every day you can cook double and freeze the extra. Do you like to bake in large quantities? A large stock of cakes in the freezer can last for many Shabbosim. Do unexpected guests drop by often? Frozen meals will prove invaluable.

If you cook every day, your freezer should be stocked with chicken, fish, checked grains, sifted flour, and the like. If you are on a minimal cooking system, relying heavily on ready-made foods, then your freezer would best be used for convenience foods such as hot dogs, pareve schnitzel, fish sticks, pastry dough and frozen vegetables.

It isn't necessary to hoard bread if your husband brings home a fresh loaf every morning, or to stock up on chicken when weekly delivery is available free of charge. Take care not to jam your freezer with unnecessary items.

ᰄ The Rebbetzin's Disaster

Cooking every day was impossible for a busy Rebbetzin with six children, three grandchildren who spent most of their time in her house, and responsibilities to her husband, the rav of a small shul. Rebbetzin Benson decided to make better use of her large freezer so she wouldn't have to cook everyday. Reviewing her busy schedule, she set aside a large block of time for a cook-in and bake-in. Monday morning arrived and she began to work. After setting a pot of water on the stove to boil, she started preparing the casseroles. But somehow, cutting the vegetables for so many casseroles and a large pot of soup took longer than expected. When she finally got to the challah she discovered that her mixer could not knead a double batch and she had to knead it by hand. And more bad news — when she took out the two chocolate cakes from the oven she tasted too much salt. It quickly became apparent that Rebbetzin Benson's recipes were not ones which could be doubled with ease: the casseroles took twice as long to make, her mixer couldn't accommodate the large volume of dough and her chocolate cake recipe couldn't be doubled without adjusting the salt. After carefully tending to the soup she remembered that her sister tried to freeze the same potato-vegetable soup and it came out tasting like glue. After four-and-a-half hours of hard work, her kitchen was piled high with dishes, pots, pans and accumulated garbage, and her children were about to come home any minute. She was so overwhelmed, she didn't know where to begin. With a sinking heart, Rebbetzin Bensen realized she had nothing to show for all of her hard work. "I'll do it differently next time," she promised herself as she turned to the sink of dirty dishes.

❦ ❦ ❦

No matter what you freeze, you must know whether it freezes well and how long it can stay frozen without deteriorating. When you decide to cook and freeze in large quantities be sure to use recipes which can be doubled or tripled without adversely affecting the results. Some foods, such as egg-based items and potatoes, change texture when frozen. Cutting vegetables and fruit is time-consuming; set aside a large block of time to do it. While in the midst of a cook-in or bake-in try to wash up as you work so that you're not left with a mountain of dishes at the end.

✺ An Unforgettable Simchas Torah

I'll never forget one particular Simchas Torah, and neither will any of our guests. My mother, a classic European, had spent the summer with me and had filled the freezer with all types of delicacies. As English wasn't her native language I had labeled most of the packages; unfortunately, a few bags were stuffed inside before I noticed them.

Two extra *bochurim* made their way to my house *erev Simchas Torah* which was also *erev Shabbos*. In a last-minute effort to find some more food to put on the *blech* I quickly inspected my freezer for something suitable. I found a small bag containing a mixture that resembled stuffing. Although the texture seemed slightly off, I didn't have time to examine it closely, so I just threw it into my huge stuffed turkey and placed it on the *blech* before I lit Shabbos and Yom Tov candles.

That night, after ten *hakafos*, there were eight hungry *bochurim* gracing our table. After serving the appetizer I entered the kitchen to prepare the main course for the table. My joy quickly dissipated as I started to spoon out the stuffing and realized it smelled like butter. Upon closer inspection, I nearly collapsed when I discovered that I was serving my mother's dairy *shlishkas* from the innards of my cooked turkey.

After my husband returned with a negative answer from the rav, I laid the turkey to rest in the garbage pail. In its place I was forced to serve the roast meat which was to have been the main course for the following day. The foods prepared for third meal became the stand-ins for our lunch, while my third meal consisted of challah. The experience changed my freezing habits forever.

When freezing items it is important to properly package and label the food. Proper packaging prevents freezer burn and keeps freshness in. Labeling packages with a date is important so you know when to use it before it spoils. We often think we'll remember what's in the opaque container or we'll recognize it in a see-through plastic bag, only to find ourselves standing at the freezer door, wondering what's in the container we just found lodged at the back of the highest shelf.

Keep a written list of all the foods you freeze. This is important because it will save you time, making your life much easier during those stressful periods when you need a quick meal. Instead of rummaging through the freezer pulling everything out, just check your list. Need to restock? Just look at the list. No more searching for that frozen chicken on *erev Shabbos*, only to discover you have to buy more.

STEP FIVE — AT A GLANCE

1. Create a cooking schedule. Decide whether you will: cook fresh every day, cook double and freeze extra, cook three times a week and save leftovers for the next day or cook once a week for the entire week.

2. An efficient food system contains four elements: a) food list; b) menu plan; c) properly organized recipes; d) shopping list.

3. Have a list of emergency Shabbos menus available for both you and your husband.

4. Be aware of how long it takes you to peel the vegetables, clean the chicken, prepare cake batter, and so forth.

5. Cook Shabbos efficiently — recipes which contain the same ingredients should be prepared and cooked simultaneously instead of cooking at separate times.

6. Plan to finish all Shabbos cooking and food preparation early on Friday morning.

7. Know which foods freeze well and the length of their freezer life.

8. Use recipes which can be doubled or tripled without adversely affecting the results.

9. When preparing meals for freezing, take into account the time spent on packaging and labeling as well as cooking time.

10. Compile a list to keep track of what you have stored in the freezer.

11. Label and date each package for freezing.

12. Place clean fresh food in airtight container or plastic bag.

13. Leave space for expansion of liquids which occurs during the freezing process.

14. Don't overcook food to be frozen.

See Appendix C for more freezer tips.

SECTION II:

ORGANIZING YOUR FAMILY

Chapter One
Shabbos and Holidays

I t was just after the kids helped serve the main course, when my four year old spilled gravy on the floor, my three year old fingered every piece of chicken on the serving plate, and the baby spit up on my lap, that I saw "the look" in our guest Sarah's eyes. She had that far-off, dreamy look that said, "My house isn't going to be like this . . . When the guests arrive everything will be ready. I'm going to serve freshly baked challahs and a homemade cake — none of this store-bought stuff. The table will be set with a shining silver *becher* and matching glasses. My kids will be dressed in clean Shabbos clothes — no holes in the tights, of course. They'll politely greet the guests, then sing 'Shalom Aleichem' with their father and quietly listen to kiddush. . ."

Several years later. . .

It had been an uneventful *erev Shabbos* and Mrs. Sarah Schwartz was proud of her accomplishments. The house was clean, the basics were cooked and she was dressed. Rivky and Faigi were also dressed and playing at a neighbor's house. The challahs, fresh from the bakery, were warming on the Shabbos urn. A pockmarked silver *becher* crowned the table, and a pot-pourri of silverware and mismatched plates completed the "setting." Best of all, she was still ten minutes early for candle light-ing.

Sarah was busy dressing the baby when her two year old called out that she hadn't reached the bathroom in time. The incriminat-ing evidence formed a pool right in the middle of the living room floor. Quickly leaving the baby, she threw a towel over the puddle, admonishing two-year-old Chani to be more careful. Just then there was a knock at the door — her Shabbos guests had arrived. Following hasty introductions, Sarah rushed back to finish dress-ing the crying baby. Returning to the living room she found Chani, tights and dress still dripping, sitting comfortably in the lap of one of the guests.

Back to square one. With Chani changed from head to toe, Sarah finally finished setting the table. Just in time, as the two older girls came running in, beaming chocolate covered smiles. Rivki's new white tights had a hole in them. That's when she saw the two guests exchange knowing glances; they had that funny gleam in their eyes. . .

❦ ❦ ❦

৶§ Shabbos

Anyone who has ever prepared for Shabbos, especially with children underfoot, knows the extent of organization and effort involved. No matter how long Friday is, there never seems to be enough time. All too often, emergencies arise. We all sense the difference in the home's atmosphere on those Fridays when everything is finished on time, in contrast to those dreaded Fridays when it's twenty minutes after candle lighting time, the dishes are still piled up in the sink and we are searching frantically for a place to hide the unfolded laundry. A calm, pleasant Friday bears no resemblance to those overwrought, frenzied slides into Shabbos. Furthermore, it is obvious that the way we prepare for Shabbos affects our entire Shabbos. Even more significant, it reflects to our families how important that day is to us. Advance planning thus becomes not only an organizational tool but an educational one as well, carrying the spirit of Shabbos into our homes throughout the entire week. The peace and light we usher in with candle lighting illuminates our household.

One of the most helpful tools of Shabbos organization is a general list of every job that should be done for Shabbos: included are folding and putting away laundry, ironing, polishing silver, cutting pieces of aluminum foil, putting away *muktzeh* items and toys, cooking, and opening bottles, cans and packages. This list in itself helps you with scheduling, delegation of jobs, and meal planning, and prevents you from omitting tasks.

Add to your list any extra jobs which must be done that week. Know what time Shabbos starts, then aim to finish an hour early. That way, you'll probably finish just on time. An extraordinary *balabusta* revealed to me her secret of success on *erev Shabbos*: she never undertook anything extra on Friday. If she finished early, she resisted the urge to make another kugel or salad; instead, she read to her children or took a nap. Some women never cook after *chatzos* or do laundry on Friday.

The following is a sample general preparation list:

(Starred items (*) can be done any time during the week. In most cases, the rest of the items can be taken care of only on *erev Shabbos*. Items marked with a (**) can be omitted in emergency situations when you don't have enough time.)

Shabbos clothes ironed *

Laundry put away **

Toys picked up, *muktzeh* toys away

Floor washed or carpet vacuumed **

Tables and chairs wiped down **
Outside of fridge, kitchen cabinets, stove top wiped off **
Turn off fridge and other non-essential lights
Tape over light switches
Dishes washed and put away **
Bathrooms cleaned — toilets, bathtub, sink, tiles **
Diapers prepared *
Tea essence made
Hot water prepared
Toilet paper torn *
Shabbos clock set
Food warmed on *blech*
Bottles, cans, packages opened *
Kiddush cup polished **
Shoes polished**

Using this list, try to schedule any job that can be done in advance for earlier in the week, leaving only a minimum of chores for Friday. For example, laundering and ironing Shabbos clothing can be done on Sunday or Monday. Cut toilet paper on Tuesday. Bake or cook on Thursday, or at least prepare everything in advance so it's ready to put in the pot.

Delegate jobs and get your whole family involved in Shabbos preparations. Even small children can pick up their toys, open the stickers on diapers, or carry silverware and other unbreakables to the table. Set realistic standards. Make your expectations clear and set a specific time for them to help. If you request help cheerfully, your children will participate enthusiastically in the Shabbos preparations and you will feel that they are a help instead of a hindrance. As they grow older, the help they offer can be more extensive. Let them choose which jobs they prefer, taking into consideration what is the most helpful to you. Most important, the work should be done in the spirit of Shabbos. It shouldn't be drudgery. I know families who involved their children at a young age and today their pre-teenage daughters bake challahs and cakes, their sixteen year olds complete the rest of the meal and their teenage sons wash the floor.

The following is a sample Shabbos delegation chart.

FAMILY SHABBOS CHART

JOB	WHO	WHEN
PICK UP TOYS	SHIRA, AGE 4	THURS. 5 P.M. & FRI. 4 P.M.
POLISH SHOES	YAAKOV, AGE 8	THURS. 5 P.M.
WASH FLOORS	IMMA	THURS. 4 P.M.

If you have small children and toddlers in the house, it's invaluable to plan ahead. A game saved just for Fridays, a special treat, a nap, an outing with an older sibling or baby sitter, relaxes them and minimizes the pressure on you. We do not want our children to dread Friday. Try to set aside a special time (even ten minutes), possibly after school, to give them extra attention. This can go a long way towards preventing frustration (both for you and for them!) as the busy day picks up speed.

Everyone will feel and behave better if he has eaten lunch. Food which doesn't require cooking and is served on disposable dishes provides fast nourishment. Some possibilities are cold cereal with milk, sandwiches, tuna salad, cheese and crackers, fruit with cream, cottage cheese with tomato and cucumber, and yogurt.

No matter how well we plan, emergencies and unforeseen obstacles will always crop up, especially with Shabbos preparations. It is important to have an emergency plan, to fulfill your minimum goals. You might decide that in case of an emergency you will either buy Shabbos food, make an easy-to-cook Shabbos (as suggested in the meal-management chapter), or rely on prepared Shabbos meals you have put away in your freezer. Whatever you decide, it must be something you can fall back on easily.

Not only *erev Shabbos* but Shabbos itself can be enhanced with proper organization and advance planning. Decide ahead of time when you will have guests and how many you will have. Will you invite *bochurim*, female students, married couples, or your children's friends? Are you too tired for guests on Friday night? Do you have room for guests to sleep over or do you prefer having visitors for just one meal? Can you accept unexpected company as late as Friday or does that overly complicate your Shabbos preparations? Does your whole family enjoy going out for a meal? Maybe your daughter would like to spend Shabbos at a friend's house, or at her grandmother's or aunt's house. (Setting policy enables everyone to know what they can expect.)

Is there a Shabbos group that your children would like to join? (The added benefit: a little time for yourself!) Have a special sweet reserved for before candle-lighting time or for Shabbos afternoon when you nap. Food treats can keep little ones occupied for quite a while. Setting out cake on Friday night that the children can help themselves to in the morning may allow you extra sleeping time.

In order to make Shabbos more enjoyable for everyone, set aside special games, books and toys to be used only on Shabbos. The anticipation of playing with that special Shabbos toy will keep children looking forward to Shabbos all week long.

Interesting stories or activities at the Shabbos table are not only educational, they help children to sit for extended periods of time. A successful teacher adapts stories from the parashah to impart Torah hashkafah to his children.

Below are a few games suitable for Shabbos:

- Kosherland or other Jewish game
- Colorforms
- Jewish holiday card game (available in English and Hebrew)
- "I know a mitzvah that has to do with hands, eyes, money, shoes. . ."
- "I went to Yerushalayim and took along. . ." Each player adds an item to a list: i.e., siddur, siddur and shoes, and so on.
- Choose a word and find the verse it's found in. Relate it to the parashah.
- Choose a personality from Tanach and let each child try to guess who it is.

Let the children put on a play based on a theme from the weekly parashah. Instead of quizzing the children on the parashah, encourage them to ask you questions. Reward them for excellent questions.

Another useful item is a Shabbos shelf or box containing opened band aids, extra hair clips, bottle opener, pre-cut aluminum foil and other articles which are often put away with *muktzeh* objects.

Remember to keep your standards and expectations realistic and flexible. If something isn't working for you, change tactics. Your closets needn't be replenished with fresh, folded laundry as long as the Shabbos clothes are ready to wear. Clean unfolded laundry can be placed in bags and deposited in a closet until *Motzaei Shabbos*. Dirty laundry which is left in the hamper can be moved to an unused location. Your kitchen floor need not be surgically clean. Every single toy on the floor doesn't have to be picked up. Dirty dishes can be put out of sight. . .and mind. What's important is to remember the significance of Shabbos, and not just the hard work, as we continue to strive toward the ultimate Shabbos of redemption.

◦§ Yom Tov: Rosh Hashanah, Yom Kippur, Succos, Simchas Torah, Purim, Shavuos

Somehow, we manage to make it through each day. We know that if things don't quite work out today, there is always tomorrow. Shabbos takes a bit more planning and effort, but since it comes every week we've already established a routine. The Yomim Tovim, however, present a tremendous challenge to us as Jewish homemakers.

One client of mine confessed that she never realized how much she juggled her myriad responsibilities every *erev chag* until last Succos when her husband went out at the last minute to purchase the *arba'a minim* and forgot to take the grocery list. There was no school that day so her three children were home as was her baby, who was suffering from an ear infection and didn't stop screaming the entire day. She was already behind in her cooking when she realized her husband hadn't finished building the *succah*. Then she discovered that her children, who had been quietly cutting pieces of paper to construct *succah* decorations, had turned their attention to the furniture and carpeting in their room — paint and glue were everywhere.

One of the reasons that preparing for the *chaggim* is more difficult than preparing for Shabbos, is that Rosh Hashanah, Succos, Purim and Yom Kippur come just once a year. You know that you have only one chance each year to make the *chag* as beautiful as possible. Then there is the time pressure. Even though cooking is allowed on Yom Tov, there are many *melachos* which are prohibited, therefore many women cook and bake before the *chag*.

An additional difficulty is that each year the day on which the *chag* falls changes, and so do your family's needs and circumstances. When last year's Pesach *seder* took place on Thursday night, everything worked out fine, but this year it falls on Friday night and so it will be harder for you. If Rosh Hashanah starts on Wednesday night, running into Shabbos, you will not only need to prepare more food, but you will also have to give more thought to activities for your family.

Arrangements that were perfect last year when you could count on your newborn to sleep and your oldest daughter to help, must change drastically now that you have a one year old toddling around, and your oldest daughter will be at her in-laws' for Yom Tov. If you ever wondered why Hashem gave you *binah yeseirah* (special female-intuition), this is the answer. It is times like these when household organization, time and meal management, *tefillah* and *siyatta dishemaya* are essential to achieving our goals.

Even at the end of a successful *chag* we are often relieved to have survived, and we frequently pray for *Mashiach* to come before we have to face the next one! It takes us a few days to recuperate and it takes us weeks to get things back to normal. Then the next Rosh Chodesh arrives, bringing with it the next Yom Tov. But there *is* a way to approach each *chag* with confidence rather than dread. Since we all own calendars, we can plot out our strategy well in advance before the holiday is at our door. My friend Shuli, for example, is the envy of everyone who knows her. No one can ever figure out how a woman who works and has such a large family can put together so many elaborate Succos decorations each year. What they fail to realize is that Shuli and her family spend many hours during the long summer vacation working on artistic projects for their *succah*. Sarah's children are always the hit of the town in their unique, professional looking Purim costumes. That's because she sits down with her children after Chanukah and asks them what their preferences are. Then they work on their outfits during the cold winter days.

Shuli and Sara have not only learned to prepare ahead in a practical, physical way, but they have also succeeded in discovering a wonderful teaching tool that involves their entire families in preparation for the holidays.

When I was a child, Pesach always left an indelible impression upon me. It was not only the great memories of the *seder*, the family gatherings and the special food that ensured this. It was also my mother's year-round policy of keeping food out of our bedrooms, thus making each one a *makom she'ain machnis bo chametz*, a place where *chametz* does not enter, which do not require a *bedikah*. Since all of us were careful to keep *chametz* out of those rooms, we were conscious of Pesach all year long.

All the Yom Tov preparations do not have to take place months in advance, however. Using many of the techniques mentioned in conjunction with *erev Shabbos*, you can ease your holiday preparations as well.

◄§ The Yom Tov Notebook

My favorite organizational tool is the Yom Tov manual. It can fill one section of a notebook or an entire file which is divided according to Yomim Tovim. You can mark down or file successful menus, game ideas, schedules (what time shul ends on Rosh Hashanah, for example), reminders (don't buy green beans for Pesach — they may be considered *kitniyos;* prohibitions on *chol hamo'ed,* and so on) and any other helpful information. Why make a new *shalach manos* list each year? Last year's list, complete with addresses and best route of delivery, saves time and energy. Add on any newcomers to the list. You can include the storage location of your Purim costumes and *succah* decorations as well as ideas for Succos decorations you think of in January. Some super-*balabustas* may not need a notebook, but for those of us trying to keep our heads above water, it is a veritable lifesaver. The following is a list of questions and suggestions to help you fill in your own Yom Tov notebook:

I. Elul
   A. Add inspiration by going to *shiurim* or listening to tapes pertinent to the *Yamim Noraim.*

II. Rosh Hashanah
   A. Menu Plan
      1. How many guests?
      2. Little time to heat up food second night Yom Tov; there are dishes to wash, table to set, all within a short time span.
      3. How to heat *seudah* if everyone (including you) is in shul all morning: put everything on a *blech* before leaving the house or leave shul forty minutes before *davening* ends. With all this in mind, a menu must be prepared (i.e., recipes suitable for extended heating time, or meals that are tasty when served at room temperature, or foods which can be re-heated quickly).
   B. Shopping
      1. Make list: (chicken/meat/fish/fish head)
      2. Vegetables and fruit including *simanim:* pomegranate, black-eyed peas, apples, carrots, dates, etc.
      3. Grocery items including honey, treats for children to keep them satisfied during long morning.
   C. *Davening*
      1. Shul/Home
         a. Where to hear the shofar? Who will watch the younger children when you go?
         b. Home alone with the kids all morning? You will need

games and activities to keep everyone occupied. Get together with a friend; each of you will have time to *daven.*

III. Yom Kippur
  A. After Rosh Hashanah, find time for a tape, *shiur* or book on *teshuvah.*
  B. *Erev Yom Kippur* is a busy time — there are many *minhagim* and a large *seudah* to eat. Try to cook the day before, or earlier and freeze.
  C. Meals needed:
    1. *Seudah mafsekes*
    2. Food for children on Yom Kippur day
    3. Meal after the fast.
  D. Note any foods that made the fast difficult (e.g., salt in chicken soup) and anything that made the fast easier (i.e. drinking water every hour from early morning until *erev Yom Kippur,* especially for nursing mothers; eating grapes, taking vitamins, and so forth).
  E. Consider purchasing elegant paper plates for the *seudah mafsekes* to eliminate having to wash a stack of dishes before the fast. Paper plates and cups can be used for children on Yom Kippur.
  F. Will the shul have a supervised play room for children? If all your children are small, can you hire a baby sitter for part of the day? Maybe invite an older girl (relative, seminary girl) to stay with you and take turns *davening* in shul.
  G. Set aside special toys or plan activities to occupy children during the day.

IV. Succos
  A. Take out decorations from last year and evaluate them.
  B. Make new decorations if needed.
  C. In addition to cake, prepare crackers and dips and other *mezonos* foods to serve in the *succah.*
  D. *Chol Hamo'ed*
    1. Remember to set aside money for *chol hamo'ed* outings.

2. When planning meals and/or outings, remember that everything takes longer than you planned. Guests tend to come late.
3. Keep list of successful outings. Add ideas. Collect project ideas to keep children occupied so you can *daven* and get the cooking done.

V. Simchas Torah
   A. Need flag or toy Torah scroll for children
   B. *Hakafos* schedules differ from shul to shul; find out your husband's schedule
   C. If you will not be staying in shul the entire time, prearrange a time for husband to dance *hakafos* with children.
   D. Avoid misunderstandings and frazzled nerves. Inform guests as to what time you will be eating.

VI. Chanukah
   A. The children are usually on vacation from school. Plan the week accordingly.
   B. If you work, what special arrangements must be made?
   C. Make latkes or doughnuts.
      1. Find recipes.
      2. Buy ingredients.
   D. If presents or treats are an integral part of your Chanukah, remember to buy them beforehand.
   E. Don't forget to buy oil or candles for the menorah.

VII. Purim
   A. If you have saved costumes from the year before, take out and try on children. They may need alterations.
   B. Make or buy additional costumes as needed.
   C. How many *shalach manos* plates do you plan to give? Make a list of addresses, arranged according to best route of delivery to prevent backtracking.
   D. Make a list of *shalach manos* ideas (e.g., small challahs, home-made jam, dried fruit, and so on) and suggestions for containers (strawberry boxes, plastic soda bottles, paper bowls, baskets, and the like).

E. Find out when and where the *megillah* is to be read in order to avoid last minute pandemonium. Leave small children with husband, older sibling, friend or baby sitter.

F. A commentary you enjoy reading on the *megillah* will greatly enhance your Purim.

G. Compile a guest list. Based on the number of people coming and whether or not they will be drinking (to fulfill *ad delo yada*), decide upon menu plan and whether or not to use paper plates and plastic cups. Remove fragile items from dining room (take out rug if possible).

H. *Shalach manos* foods suitable for Shabbos (i.e., kugels, cakes, fish) are particularly appreciated when Purim falls on *erev Shabbos*. Make extra so you can benefit from these delicacies at your own Shabbos table as well.

I. Have children prepare *shalach manos* cards (such as "A *freilichen Purim* from the Cohens"). If you have included homemade items, note which *hechsherim* you have relied upon and whether everything is absolutely pareve, or pareve but baked in a *fleishig* or *milchig* oven, for example. After all, you've put your heart and soul into the *shalach manos* — you want the recipients to enjoy them.

J. Purim is often a truly topsy-turvy day when heaps of *shalach manos* accumulate in your kitchen. If you've properly labeled and packed your goodies, they won't end up in the garbage pail. (For example, an unlabeled potato kugel arrives. Your family only enjoys it served hot. You have no idea in which oven to heat it or whether it can be served with *fleishig*. If you haven't kept the card which tells you who sent it, then you won't be able to clarify the problem, so you might end up just throwing it out. What a waste of good food and intentions!)

K. Prepare *shaloch manos* plates for unanticipated arrivals — wrapped and ready, as if you had expected them. Food items thrown together hastily usually appear as if they were haphazard, and this can be insulting.

VIII. Pesach — See page 121.

IX. Shavuos
   A. Include a dairy selection — either a whole meal or simply a *milchig* kiddush. Don't forget the cheesecake.
   B. Prepare cake and a thermos of coffee or tea for those who will be learning through the night.
   C. Plan how you will keep small children occupied during the day so as not to disturb the sleep of family members and guests who were learning all night.

⋖§ Pesach

For many women, Pesach cleaning confirms their status as slaves still awaiting liberation. The mere mention of Pesach elicits a panic-stricken response as memories of last year's turmoil spring to mind. Who can forget the non-stop running from room to room, and closet to closet. Or the child who dropped crumbs into the pail of rinse water just as it was poured onto the kitchen floor, or the cookie crumbs discovered in bed on the night of *bedikas chametz*? Yes, after all that hard work and effort many of us wish Pesach lasted more than one week. We hope this section will make *erev Pesach* not quite so "memorable."

⋖§ What to Clean

The first and most important step in Pesach preparation is to approach the overwhelming aspect of cleaning by breaking each job down into small, manageable tasks. Look over the following list of items that must be cleaned or checked for *chametz* and add your particular requirements. Once every task is listed and categorized by room, your Pesach cleaning will seem less mind-boggling. Last-minute surprises will be almost entirely eliminated.

The *mitzvah* is to rid the house of *chametz*; spring cleaning is not mandatory before Pesach. Washing the ceilings, washing the tops of window panes and reorganizing storage closets that no one ever uses can be left for a less hectic time of year. Be clear as to what is halachically required and what are the extras. Keep in mind that you can sell a closet, cupboard or storage area which you will not use during the holiday.

The following is a room-to-room cleaning list:

I. Basement, porch, attic or garage
II. Master bedroom
    A. Closets
        1. All sides and doors
        2. Clothes
        3. Underneath and on top
    B. Beds
        1. Frame
        2. Mattress
        3. Blankets, sheets pillows
        4. Underneath
    C. Chest
        1. Drawers
        2. Clothes
    D. Radiator
    E. Wall
    F. Door
    G. Windows
    H. Carpet
III. Children's room
    A. Closets
        1. All sides
        2. Clothes
        3. Underneath
    B. Bed, crib
        1. Frame
        2. Mattress
        3. Blankets, sheets, pillows
        4. Underneath
    C. Stroller or Carriage
    D. Toys

    E. Books

    F. Radiator

    G. Walls

    H. Door

    I. Windows

    J. Carpet

IV. Dining Room and Living Room

    A. Books and Bookshelves

    B. Buffet

    C. Dining Room Table and Chairs

    D. Couch and Chairs

    E. Radiator

    F. Wall

    G. Doors

    H. Windows

    I. Carpet

V. Kitchen

    A. Cabinets

        1. All sides

        2. Items

    B. Pantry

        1. All sides

        2. Remove food containing *chametz*

        3. Wipe off each item

    C. Appliances

        1. Refrigerator

        2. Freezer

        3. Oven

        4. Stovetop

        5. Toaster

        6. Mixer

        7. Blender

        8. Food processor

        9. Microwave

    D. Kitchen table and chairs

    E. High chair

F. Counter top, tiles, faucets, sinks
G. Radiator
H. Walls
I. Door
J. Windows
K. Floor
VI. Bathroom
    A. Medicine cabinet (separate contents into three boxes labeled: *chametz,* non-*chametz,* and questionable)
    B. Sink
    C. Bathtub
    D. Toilet
    E. Hamper
    F. Washing Machine, Dryer
    G. Rug
    H. Radiator
    I. Wall
    J. Doors
    K. Windows
    L. Floor
VII. Floors

Once your list is tailored to your own home, you are in a position to decide what needs to be done and who can help. What will your husband do? What can your ten or twelve year old do? Will your four year old wash her own toy dishes or should you put them away for the *chag*? What about hired help?

Don't be afraid to involve children in Pesach preparations. In addition to teaching them how to clean for Pesach, their participation will generate excitement and enthusiasm for the approaching holiday. Knowing they are an integral part of the cleaning squad builds self-confidence and fortitude. Especially if tasks are delegated in an upbeat manner, positive feelings will be created.

When children are given a choice as to their preference of jobs, they will meet the challenge much more willingly. Provide detailed instructions: explain to them what has to be done, what standards are expected of them, and when the task is to be performed. Supply the proper cleaning equipment. A family cleaning chart can be drawn up with each person's name and the assigned task stated clearly. Post it in a central location. The following is a sample:

NAME	PLACE	HOW TO DO IT	DATE
THE FAMILY CLEANING CHART			
SHAINA, 10 & PENINA, 12	A. BEDROOM CLOSET	A. TAKE OUT YOUR CLOTHES AND CHECK POCKETS, BRUSHING SEAM WITH A SMALL NAIL BRUSH. B. REMOVE CONTENTS OF DRAWERS AND SHAKE OUT AND CHECK POCKETS AS ABOVE C. CHECK ITEMS TO BE PLACED BACK IN DRAWER.	
	B. SHELVES	A. GO THROUGH BOOKS. B. WIPE DOWN SHELVES.	
	C. BEDS	A. VACUUM MATTRESSES. B. WIPE BED FRAMES.	
	D. CARPET.	A. VACUUM	BY 1 NISAN
BRACHA, 17	A. BOTTOM KITCHEN CUPBOARDS	A. TAKE OUT POTS AND PANS AND INSPECT FOR CHAMETZ. B. PUT BACK IN ORDERLY FASHION	BY 4 NISAN
SHIMON, 16	STOVE TOP AND OVEN	A. SPRAY ON OVEN CLEANER. SOAK STOVE TOP WITH BLEACH.	ON 10 NISAN
TZVI, 8	YOUR DESK DRAWER	A. TAKE OUT PAPERS. B. TURN DRAWER UPSIDE DOWN OVER TRASH CAN AND SHAKE IT OUT. C. BRUSH OUT PAYING ATTENTION TO CORNERS.	BY 8 NISAN

❧ Creating a Pesach Cleaning Schedule

Some women begin with their kitchen cupboards and areas of the kitchen not used on a daily basis. Early progress made in the kitchen provides a psychological boost. Homemakers can get the Yom Tov cooking under way while the rest of the house undergoes final "mopping up " activities. Other women prefer to start by cleaning those places which are less likely to contain substantial amounts of *chametz* (such as the bedrooms) and then move on to the real challenge. There are those who work simultaneously in both areas of the house, especially if older children are working with them.

Whatever tactics you employ, you need a plan in order to arrive (in one piece) at the *seder* table. A carefully drawn-up time schedule will get you there sane and sound. However, even the most well thought-out program may need periodic reassessment. Is work going too slowly? Maybe your cleaning equipment is unsatisfactory. Are you using the most effective detergent? Are you washing with a soft cloth when you need something more abrasive, such as Scotchbrite or steel wool? Should you be employing a spray bottle rather than a rag dipped in cleaning solution to get into tight corners? Efficient cleaning methods and determination will set you in motion.

Are interruptions your downfall? Toys and games put aside for these special days will go a long way towards keeping children occupied. Leave food and drink on the kitchen table for the children to help themselves, so that you can continue cleaning undisturbed. If they show interest, let your children in on the action. Young children love to clean their own toys. Fill the bathtub with soapy water and let them scrub. If they continue to distract you after you've tried these suggestions then consider hiring a baby sitter (your peace of mind is well worth the cost).

Is the telephone your undoing? A cordless phone or one with a long cord enables you to continue cleaning as you speak. Heavy discussions could be rescheduled for a later hour when you can concentrate on the conversation. Or . . . take the phone off the hook.

If your schedule is too tightly packed and Pesach is around the corner, get extra help! Ask a Rav what areas of the house may be sold instead of cleaned.

Whatever your strategy, be realistic in your scheduling. Maybe it's impossible to clean an entire room in one day, but it shouldn't take more than a week. After drawing up a schedule remain flexible enough to alter your plans. For example, if you intended to clean the bed this morning and little Moishey just fell asleep on it, start working in another area.

Now is the time to create your specific time schedule. On the following page is a pre-Pesach planning calendar. You fill in the items or rooms you intend to clean, when you will shop, and when you will set up your Pesach kitchen (that is, put away *chametz* dishes, cover counters and cabinets, take out Pesach dishes). Most people underestimate the time involved in completing these tasks. Don't forget to set aside time to cook for Pesach itself (the *seder,* Yom Tov morning, and so on). If you want to include a daily meal plan, space has been provided for you to jot that down, too.

PESACH CLEANING CALENDAR

ADAR	SUN 17	MON. 18	TUE. 19	WED. 20	THURS. 21	FRI. 22	M.S.
MORN.:							
AFT.:							
NIGHT:							
MAIN MEAL							

ADAR	SUN. 24	MON. 25	TUES. 26	WED. 27	THURS. 28	FRI. 29	M.S.
MORN.:							
AFT.:							
NIGHT:							
MAIN MEAL							

NISAN	SUN. 8	MON. 9	TUES. 10	WED. 11	THURS. 12	FRI. 13	EREV PES.
MORN.:							
AFT.:							
NIGHT:							
MAIN MEAL							

PESACH CLEANING CALENDAR

` ADAR	SUN 17	MON. 18	TUE. 19	WED. 20	THURS. 21	FRI. 22	M.S.
MORN.:	PORCH STORAGE ROOM SHOP FOR PESACH	MASTER BEDROOM	MASTER BEDROOM	FINISH MASTER BEDROOM	COOK FOR SHABBOS	CLEAN FOR SHABBOS	
AFT.:	COOKING, LAUNDRY, ATTEND TO CHILDREN				FINISH ALL LAUNDRY		
NIGHT:	DISHES, READ AND RELAX						
MAIN MEAL	CHICKEN SALAD LEFTOVER SALADS	FRIED BAKALA RICE WITH VEGETABLES	ZUCHINI CASSEROLE	CHICKEN BURGERS	CHEESE QUICHE	SHABBOS MEAL	

ADAR	SUN. 24	MON. 25	TUES. 26	WED. 27	THURS. 28	FRI. 29	M.S.
MORN.:	BOY'S ROOM	BOY'S ROOM	BOY'S ROOM	GIRL'S ROOM	GIRL'S ROOM	CLEAN FOR SHABBOS	
AFT.:	COOKING, LAUNDRY, ATTEND TO CHILDREN				FINISH ALL LAUNDRY	COOK FOR SHABBOS	
NIGHT:	DISHES, RELAX						
MAIN MEAL	LEFTOVERS	FISH STEW	TUNA CASSEROLE	TURKEY GOULASH	PIZZA	SHABBOS MEAL	

NISAN	SUN. 1	MON. 2	TUES. 3	WED. 4	THURS. 5	FRI. 6	M.S.
MORN.:	GIRL'S ROOM	LIVING ROOM	LIVING ROOM	KITCHEN CABINETS	KITCHEN CABINETS	CLEAN FOR SHABBOS	
AFT.:	COOKING, LAUNDRY, ATTEND TO CHILDREN				FINISH LAUNDRY	COOK FOR SHABBOS	
NIGHT:	DISHES, READ AND RELAX						
MAIN MEAL	LEFTOVERS	CASSEROLE	BURGERS W/ VEG.	TURKEY SCHNITZEL	PIZZA W/ SALAD	SHABBOS MEAL	

NISAN	SUN. 8	MON. 9	TUES. 10	WED. 11	THURS. 12	FRI. 13	EREV PES.
MORN.:	FRIDGE	STOVE	FINISH KITCHEN	SHOP FOR PESACH COOK	SHOP FOR PERISHABLES COOK		
AFT.:	COOKING, LAUNDRY, ATTEND TO CHILDREN				FINISH LAUNDRY		
NIGHT:	STUDY HAGGADAH						
MAIN MEAL	LEFTOVERS	BAKED POTATO WITH CHEESE AND SALAD	FISH AND RICE	CHICKEN AND POTATOES	TOMATO WITH MELTED CHEESE		

Cleaning Equipment

Have you ever run out of oven cleaner after spraying one side of your oven? Well I have, so just to make sure that it doesn't happen to either of us, here is a basic list of cleaning equipment. Add anything else you need:

bleach or ammonia
broom
cleaning rags
floor rags
furniture polish
gloves
mop
oven cleaner
scotchbrite
scrub brush
soap
spray bottle
steel wool
toothbrush
two buckets or basins
window cleaner

᳚ Keeping Chametz Out

Discovering *chametz* in an area you've already cleaned for Pesach can be very irritating. How can this be avoided? Let's begin by investigating the scientific characteristics of *chametz*. Despite popular opinion, *chametz* possesses neither wings nor legs, but don't underestimate it . . . it's smart. Due to its handicaps, *chametz* is always on the lookout for a free ride. Once it is brought into a house, there is no reliable way to ascertain where it will end up. *Chametz* often slips unnoticed onto an unsuspecting sleeve, and after leaving the kitchen keeps an eye out for another interesting part of "town." The dark and mysterious cushions of the living room couch are a favorite spot. Sometimes, *chametz* is forced into a coat pocket and imprisoned in the closet. Other times, it sneaks into a skirt pleat or shirt cuff. Either way that nasty *chametz* soon infiltrates our entire home. Just what can be done to put an end to its wanderings? Because *chametz* operates as a parasite, we must raise human awareness. Form a "Stop *Chametz* Now" campaign. All *chametz* lovers should be instructed to dispose of their *chametz* before entering cleaned zones.

To start your campaign you need a number of strategies. Here are a few:

After cleaning a room, use it as infrequently as possible. For example, once the the master bedroom is done, steer all activities away from there; sew, read, relax, and so forth, in another room. Each person should shake himself off before entering the cleaned room.

When the family is eating in the kitchen, keep the door closed. Ask everyone to shake himself off thoroughly before leaving. Some women substitute pita for bread because it makes less crumbs. Other women require sandwiches to be eaten outside (such as on a porch, or outside the apartment building). Serving non-*chametz* meals is also helpful (for suggestions see below).

On each door leading to a *kosher lePesach* area (a room or cabinet) a picture or sign can be posted as a reminder to shake off crumbs. A picture, such as a piece of bread with a big red *X* drawn over it is ideal because it is suitable for both adults and children (who haven't yet learned to read). At bedtime, children can shed dirty clothes in the bathroom, putting on clean "*chametz* free" pajamas before entering their rooms. Be sure they change completely because *chametz* knows no boundaries. It even crawls beneath undershirts!

⊸§ Erev Pesach Meals

When you're completely involved in Pesach cleaning, laundry and cooking are easily forgotten. Therefore, plan simple meals, use convenience foods (such as frozen and canned goods), and remember to feed your husband, children and yourself. Everyone will feel better and calmer if they have eaten properly.

Make things easier on yourself — use paper plates, paper cups and plastic knives, forks and spoons whenever possible. Hire baby sitters and cleaning help as your budget allows. Don't hesitate to accept offers of help from seminary girls or *bochurim* who will be spending Yom Tov with you. They will have a good feeling enjoying your hospitality later when they know they contributed to the *erev Pesach* preparations.

Avoid cooking actual *chametz* during the week before Pesach. You'd be surprised how much food containing *kitniyos* there is, which is not actual *chametz*. Make sure to have plenty of non-*chametz* snacks on hand for the month before the *chag*. Buy snacks that contain *kitniyos;* rice crackers instead of wheat crackers, potato chips instead of pretzels, *Pesachdik* cookies instead of *chametzdik* ones.

Below is a sample list of non-*chametzdik* foods:

ᴇᔑ Pre-Pesach Food List

Snacks and Light Meals
    cheese, chocolate, chocolate spread, cold cuts, date spread, honey, hot dogs, ice cream, jam, nuts, peanut butter, pudding, raisins, rice cakes, yellow cheese, yogurt

Canned Goods
    chumus, fruit, olives, pickles, techina, tuna, vegetables,

Fruit and Vegetables

A few meal planning ideas:
    Breakfast:
        puffed rice cereal
        cornflakes
        peanut butter and jam on rice cakes
        cottage cheese and vegetables
    Lunch:
        tuna salad and potato salad
        mashed potatoes w/cheese and cucumber salad
        omelet with melted yellow cheese

Dinner:
    Shabbos leftovers
    baked potato w/cheese and salad
    chicken and potatoes
    fish and rice

◄§ Pesach Shopping and Cooking

Pesach shopping and cooking can be made easier by using a meal planning system. Compose a menu plan (including all the meals you will serve during the week of Pesach). Then write a shopping list based on the menu plan. Include the many cakes and snacks you think you'll need. So many new, kosher-for-Pesach products are introduced on the market every year that it is tempting to splurge on these costly items. A shopping list will help you overcome this temptation. Be sure to shop early before you find nothing left on the shelves. Also order matzah early so as not to have a problem. A menu plan will enable you to make the most of your time once you finish cleaning the kitchen. With gefilte fish, soup, or cake already in your freezer as you enter the holiday, Pesach itself will be much more relaxing. The following is a sample shopping list of Pesach goods:

◄§ Pesach Shopping List

Cleaning items and Paper products
    baking paper, candles, detergent, dish soap, dish sponge, dishwashing soap, matches, napkins, paper plates/bowls/ cups, paper towels, plastic bags (small/med/large), plastic silverware, Scotchbrite, shampoo, soap, steel wool, tin foil, tissues, toilet paper, toothbrush, toothpaste

Miscellaneous Food Stuffs
    coffee, tea, jam, oil, sugar, matzah, matzah meal, potato flour, almonds, walnuts, baking powder, date spread, raisins, coconut, chocolate, candy, cookies, cake mixes, mayonnaise, ketchup, salad dressing, apple juice, orange juice

Fruits
apples (red and green), bananas, grapes, grapefruit, nec-
tarines, oranges, peaches, plums, tangerines, strawberries,
apricots, pears

Vegetables
avocados, beets, carrots, celery, garlic, pepper (green and
red), lettuce, potatoes, squash, sweet potatoes, tomatoes,
eggplant, onions

Meat/Frozen Goods
chicken, chicken schnitzel, turkey shnitzel, roast/ground
meat, ground turkey, ground chicken, halibut, hake, mullet,
pike, sliced carp, sole, red snapper, whitefish

Spices
salt, pepper, cinnamon, garlic, onion powder, oregano,
paprika

Dairy and Pareve Items
butter, cream cheese, yellow cheese, eggs, leben, margarine,
milk, sour cream, plain yogurt, fruit-flavored yogurt, cottage
cheese

Utensils
dishes, silverware, pots, other

❧ ❧ ❧

Now that you're ready to begin the actual work, put on your
favorite cleaning outfit and turn on some music or an inspira-
tional *shiur*. Bizechus *nashim tzidkanios nigalu mi'Mitzrayim*,
"Through the merit of righteous women we were redeemed from
Egypt." This year may we all be *zoche* to bring the *geulah.*

Chapter Two
Gaining Your Child's Cooperation
— An Inside View

It's 5:40 p.m. Your four children ages 3, 5, 7, and 9, are all playing quietly. The house looks like Hurricane Hilda just blew over. Your husband will come home at 7:15 and you want everything in its place when he walks through the front door. Will you succeed? This is the opportunity you've been waiting for — to prove to yourself how well you can encourage your children to help clean up without too much hassle.

You're exhausted from a long hard day. After the children left for school in the morning, you cleaned up the house, then you washed the kitchen floor, vacuumed the living room carpet and cooked a three-course lunch in honor of your Aunt Pearl, who was planning to visit that day. She arrived promptly at one o'clock and stayed for the rest of the afternoon. The children enjoyed her company — especially because of the presents she showered upon them. Elisheva, the eldest, received a jewelry making center containing hundreds of assorted beads and other materials necessary for necklace production. Akiva, the seven year old, was thrilled to get an airplane kit including enough parts to build five planes. Ari, the next in line, acquired a Weeble town with a gas station, an airport, a post office, not to mention big and little Weebles. Penina, the youngest, became the proud owner of the entire Potato Head family, which she hasn't stopped playing with since she tore off the gift wrapping.

As the children play happily, you size up the job ahead of you. Aunt Pearl's presents, a substantial contribution to your children's toy chest, contain so many pieces that they form a second layer of flooring throughout the house. Both sinks are filled with dishes and pots. The living room looks a little too lived in. Attempting to enter the children's bedrooms is sheer folly; you need a bridge to cross from one end to the other. Thinking of all your hard work earlier in the day and how beautifully clean everything was just six short hours ago, you wish you could just lie down and not get up until tomorrow morning. No, you don't want your husband to walk into this mess. You remind yourself of your original resolution: you are going to whip this place into shape by 7:15 and your children are going to help!

You have two choices (pick one):
- ☐ In order to revitalize your energy you decide to rest for twenty minutes (turn to page 136).
- ☐ In order to get the ball rolling you decide to get the children moving — **now**:

Exhausted, you drag yourself into the living room where Elisheva and Akiva are playing quietly. You decide to lay it on the line. "The party's over," you announce. "This house is a wreck and it has to be whipped back into shape." You are too tired to sound authoritative and so your words don't come across as very convincing. The children continue to play. Exasperated, you stamp your foot on the carpet, but the sound comes out muffled, and the only result is a cramp in your leg. You try a different tactic. "I'm very upset that you aren't helping me clean up," you say. "Maybe I should call Aunt Pearl and tell her to take back the presents she just gave you." Elisheva and Akiva flash each other knowing glances. You march over to the phone and pick up the receiver. With one finger on the button to quiet the dial tone, you dial her number. You pretend that you hear it ringing and that she picks up on the other end. "Hello, Pearl," you begin. Then you hear the children laughing as Akiva tells Elisheva that Aunt Pearl can't possibly be home yet because it takes her two hours to drive there. At that point the phone rang. Well, that ends the "phone call" attempt. You leave the living room wondering why your children refuse to help you.

Then it occurs to you that you are too tired to establish a clear-cut plan and therefore you aren't able to delegate effectively. You neglected to speak to the children in a positive manner — in a way that will engage their cooperation. You decide to rest for twenty minutes and come up with a game plan.

You sit down in the living room with your head against a pillow and put your feet up on the footstool. It feels good to rest. You take a deep breath and the muscles in your back begin to relax. Your entire body loosens up as you close your eyes and your mind reviews the day's events. Aunt Pearl was so proud of you and your accomplishments. You are happy and silently thank Hashem for giving you such a wonderful family and comfortable home.

After ten minutes of relaxing in this manner you open your eyes and see Elisheva looking at you. She walks over and sits down next to you on the couch. You look into her deep brown eyes and ask her how she enjoyed her day. "It was great," she says enthusiastically. "I like it when you play with us all afternoon and when Aunt Pearl asks us questions about school and friends and stuff like that."

Then Akiva, who has been watching from a distance, joins in. "Me, too," he says. "I like it better when you pay attention to us, instead of running around doing laundry and talking on the telephone to your friends."

Just as he finishes speaking, Ari and Penina run in fighting over a toy. "I was playing with it," Ari shouts.

"But it's *my* turn!" Penina retorts.

They both start tugging at the miniature gas station. "Come here, Ari and Penina," you call. They approach you with their hands glued to the toy. "You both sound angry and frustrated. Ari, you want to continue playing with the toy. Penina you want to play with it now because you haven't had a turn yet. This is a problem — two children and one gas station. What should we do?"

Ari lets go of the toy. He turns to Penina. "You play with the gas station," he says. "I want to play with the post office, O.K.?"

"O.K.," Penina squeaks.

You smile lovingly. "Ari, you gave in," you comment. "What a big *mitzvah*!" Ari grins and returns to the bedroom.

Penina sits down next to you on the couch. "Why are we sitting here?" she asks.

"We are resting so that we will have energy to clean up the house," you answer.

Her eyes open wide. "Clean the house! But it's so messy." Instantly, she leaps off the couch and disappears for a minute, then returns holding the broom. "I'll sweep everything," she declares as she swings the broom handle along the floor. Green and blue beads start to roll in every direction. Elisheva runs over to Penina and attempts to remove the broom from her grasp. "No, my broom!" Penina screams.

"I don't want the broom," Elisheva tries to explain. "I want you to stop scattering my beads." She bends down next to the box, slowly collecting a few beads and placing them in their container.

Penina releases the broom and picks up a bead and a string. She asks Elisheva to help her make a necklace. Elisheva settles down comfortably and they begin to play.

You look at your watch. It's already six o'clock. You feel much better now that you've rested and you've decided it is time to swing into high gear.

You have two choices (pick one):

☐ In order to get the children to help, you encourage them in a friendly fashion (turn to page 139).

☐ In order to get the children to help, you decide it's time to become a dictator:

You stand up and march over to your nine year old. "Elisheva!" you bark. "Pick up this jewelry center NOW. When I come back in five minutes I don't want to see a single bead. You hear me? Start picking up. Hurry!" Taking no notice of her reaction, you confront Akiva. "Don't you be *chutzpadik* with me. There is no room in this house for lazy children. You should know by now that airplane models aren't built in a day, so you have to clean up after each building session. And I'm not taking responsibility for any stray pieces. If I see anything left on the floor I'm going to crush it under my shoe." You glare at him angrily to show him you mean business. As you turn to leave the living room you shout over your shoulder, "And when you're done, Elisheva, you are to go to the kitchen and scrub those dishes. I'm tired of doing your chores. You are old enough to wash dishes. Soon you are going to stop taking all my hard work for granted." You stalk out of the room without waiting for a response.

Before you launch the attack on the bedroom you brace yourself for a fight. Although it didn't seem possible, the room is in worse shape now than it was twenty minutes ago. "Ari! Penina!" you shout like an army captain, "if you two don't pick up every object in this room I'm going to take away all of your toys and put them away for good."

They begin to cry. "It's too hard," Ari whines.

"There is too much to pick up," Penina sobs. "I want to *play* toys, no pick up." You approach them menacingly and shout even louder, "PICK UP! PICK UP! If you don't pick up the toys you will both be in big trouble!"

They stand up looking defeated. "Too hard, too many toys!" Ari repeats.

"Stop acting like spoiled babies and get moving," you reply, your voice hoarse from yelling so much. They resume crying.

You hurry back to the living room to see if Elisheva and Akiva can help them, only to discover they have barely made any headway in the living room.

It seems you might have to change tactics. This strategy isn't getting the house any cleaner. The shouting is taking its toll; you are running out of steam. The children are more upset than ever and unwilling to obey your terse orders.

Perhaps friendly persuasion is the best course of action after all.

"Elisheva, Akiva, Ari, Penina," you call out in a friendly, yet firm voice. "Please come to the kitchen. I want to give you something." They all come bounding into the kitchen, happy to obtain a reprieve from the impending labor. You have just made a pitcher of apple juice and are pouring it into five cups. "Listen, troops, we have a tough hour ahead of us and we will need extra energy. A drink should do the trick." Their smiling faces let you know you are on the right track. "O.K., we need a game plan. I know we are capable of whipping this place into shape before daddy comes home. How are we going to do it? Does anyone have any suggestions?"

"What exactly has to get done?" Akiva asks hesitantly.

You resist the urge to make a sarcastic remark and respond instead, "Good question, Akiva. The most important tasks right now are to clear up the toys from the living room floor, put back the cushions on the couch and place the chairs around the table. In the boy's bedroom, the toys have to be picked up off the floor and put away in the toy cabinet. The dishes should be washed too."

They all ponder the situation for a few moments. Then Elisheva pipes up with a suggestion. "It seems to me," she says, "that either each child should pick up the toy he got as a present from Aunt Pearl while you wash the dishes, or. . . ."

"No," Akiva interrupts her, "it will go faster if we all work together in the same room."

You acknowledge Akiva's idea and ask Elisheva to finish her sentence. "That's what I was going to say, kind of," she goes on. "I was going to suggest that I supervise and we start in the living room, because daddy sees that room first. Then we can move on to the bedroom. If we finish in time, I will wash the dishes and you, Mommy, can wash the bowls, pots and pans." You think it over for a minute and declare it a deal.

Ari and Penina haven't responded yet and you get the feeling that it is going to take some extra reinforcement to ensure that the cleaning goes smoothly. You remember reading that the "right incentive at the right time" can make the difference between cooperation and reluctance. As you watch your children pour another round of drinks you review all of the options: a special food treat, star charts, mitzvah certificates (redeemable for a gift), a small trinket, a new game, a visit to a friend, a bedtime story. Since they each just received a new toy, you decide upon a combination of a story and a treat before they go to bed. "O.K., has everyone said borei nefashos?" you ask. "Let's begin as you suggested Elisheva and Akiva. When the rooms are clean I will read your favorite story, and everyone will get a special treat. It will be a surprise."

Jackpot. The children's eyes light up. They all run into the living room at once, and you follow them. "I would just like to remind everyone that last Thursday evening you all worked in an extremely organized and quick manner and cleaned up in record time," you say. "Daddy and I were amazed at your skill and intelligence in tackling a challenge. I bet you can beat last week's record tonight." The children are clearly enthusiastic about the task before them.

You have two choices (pick one):

☐ You stay with them to give them helpful guidance
(turn to page 142).
☐ You return to the kitchen to make a phone call

It took quite a lot of energy to engage the children's help in a positive manner, but your technique seems to have been successful. Now you feel you've done your part and you enter the kitchen to call a friend and tell her about your day. Before you dial Avigail's number you clear the kitchen table. Once she answers the phone the only chore you can do with the limited phone extension cord is to wash the pots in the meat sink. As she relates the day's events you listen contentedly, barely noticing how slowly you are working.

Suddenly, Penina runs in. "Ari hit me!" she says indignantly. You mutter a few words of consolation as she mopes out of the kitchen and return to the phone conversation. Avigail is pouring out her frustrations to you and although you can't get any more work done while on the phone, you don't have the heart to cut her off.

Hearing a commotion coming from the living room, you excuse yourself from the conversation for a moment, stick your head into the hall and yell out nervously, "Stop fighting. Please get back to work." The children stop arguing temporarily, but when you resume talking you can hear them quarreling in the background again.

After another ten minutes you are finally able to say goodbye to Avigail. When you peek into the living room you discover that only Penina is still working, while the rest of the cleaning crew is sitting in the corner of the room studying a photo album which they found under the couch. "Come on, kids, get moving!" you urge bleakly. But you don't feel like getting into an argument, so you leave them and head for the boys' bedroom.

There doesn't seem to be any alternative but to clean the room yourself. You get down on your hands and knees and start placing each toy in its proper container. After a short while you become frustrated as you notice the large amount of pieces left to clear up. You feel yourself getting angrier by the moment. What went wrong? The children seemed motivated when they began. Now they act as if they don't care.

Perhaps you should have started them off on the right track by showing them how to do their chores. Perhaps you should have checked on them every so often, giving them encouragement and moral support. Well, it's not too late. There is still time until your husband comes home.

You explain exactly what has to be done and see to it that everyone has picked some aspect of cleanup. You all work together. As the work progresses, before little hands begin to tire, you decide to give some positive encouragement.

"Wow!" you exclaim in admiration. "I see that most of the toys have been picked up. There isn't much left to do. Daddy will be so happy to see the room clean and to find out that you are the ones who cleaned it. I can really count on you to help me." You smile cheerfully and your voice conveys true appreciation. "There are only a few things left to be done." You glance at the toys on the floor and then at the couch, which is still in disarray. They follow your gaze and understand what you want from them.

Elisheva starts to put the couch cushions back in place. Akiva turns to Ari. "If you'll help me finish picking up the toys it will go faster," he says. Ari bends down and picks up one toy and walks across the room to place it into a small box.

"Hey, do you want to see a trick?" you ask Ari. He smiles expectantly. You gather all of the toy boxes — one for each type of toy — and place them in the middle of the room. Then you bring in the broom. "Ari," you say, "watch how much quicker it goes when you sweep all of the toys into the center of the room. You don't have to keep getting up and walking across the room to collect every single toy. Just stay in one place and put each toy in its container." As you show him how smoothly it works, Akiva starts to follow your lead. Ari joins Akiva and in a very short time the room looks presentable.

"Wonderful!" you call out. "It is a pleasure to work with such efficient and pleasant helpers."

"It wasn't so hard," Akiva comments, "and it didn't take us that long to do."

"You're right," you say. "As a matter of fact, let's have a race in the bedroom. The first to finish is the first to relax." The children run into the bedroom but confusion follows because no one knows where to start. You head in that direction and quickly survey the situation. "O.K., these are the areas that have to be attended to: on top of the beds, under the beds, in the far left corner of the room and in the center of the room. What area do you want to clean, Elisheva?"

She looks around carefully. "I want to clear off the tops of the beds," she replies.

"Good. Do you know what needs to be done?" you ask her. She answers to your satisfaction.

Then Akiva and Ari both speak up at the same time, asking to straighten up the corner of the room. "Well, you were both such good partners in the living room. Maybe the partnership could continue," you offer hopefully. Akiva shrugs his shoulders while Ari runs to the corner to start picking up. In the meantime, Penina decides that she wants to pick up the blocks in the center of the room, so you bring her the basket and she gets to work.

You don't leave the room yet. You watch each child, offering assistance and explaining the quickest and most efficient way to do each job.

With the clean-up efforts progressing to both your satisfaction and theirs, you go to the kitchen and wash the dishes in the dairy sink. Soon a chorus of voices is heard in the bedroom. Ari sails into the kitchen announcing that he finished first. "Come look, Mommy," urge the rest of the voices from the bedroom. Happily you walk to the room and step inside, greeted by the proud faces of your children.

Although the room is in good shape, you spot a few items out of place. What is your next move?

You have two choices (pick one):
- ☐ You decide to praise their hard work and accomplishments (turn to the next page).
- ☐ You decide to criticize their mistakes

The smile on your face is replaced by a look of disappointment. "*This* is what you call a clean room?" you ask in amazement. Four pairs of eyes instantly look downward. "I expected a much better job," you say as you slowly walk around the room, inspecting each area and item. "Elisheva, if this is what you call a spotless bed then I think you need glasses," you say to her. "Akiva, why are you so lazy? I see the paper you kicked under the drawers. You probably hoped I wouldn't find it. With a little more effort you could have actually put it back in its place. But I'm sure this idea didn't occur to you." Akiva fidgets with his belt. Penina looks at him in confusion. "Ari," you continue speaking, "you had the nerve to tell me that you finished first? You are such a slob. Won't you ever learn?"

You pace back and forth, casting an angry glance at each child. The room is silent except for the sound of your footsteps. Instead of becoming calmer your anger continues to grow. You are bothered by your children's incompetence. "Lazy, good-for-nothings," you mutter aloud.

Suddenly Penina starts to cry. "Mommy, I hid the papers there," she says between sobs. "I didn't want them to be thrown in the garbage. Is that why you are angry at us?" Penina continues crying. Elisheva puts her arm around Penina to comfort her.

Ari can't control himself anymore. "I'm not a slob," he shouts. "I'm not."

"If you don't want to be called a slob then I want you to finish the job you started," you say. "Elisheva, Akiva, Penina, the same goes for you."

As you stride to the door you look back over your shoulder to see Ari scratching his head and looking bewildered. The other children are shuffling around dejectedly. Although you've spoken your mind, you feel an uneasy pain in your heart. It is clear that criticism and name-calling aren't the tools most effective for motivating your children to perform more efficiently. Why make them feel like failures when they have so much potential? And now you, too, feel like a failure. After thinking about it you decide that praise and positive feedback will work better.

You enter the bedroom with a large smile, eyes sparkling and a voice singing with admiration. "I see neatly made beds, games arranged in an orderly fashion on the shelf and all of the blocks in their baskets." You spread your arms wide open and declare, "It is a real pleasure to walk into this room!" The children's eyes are shining with happiness, their faces are beaming. "Ari, are you the one who crawled under this bed to clear away the toys?" you ask. He nods his head. "That is what I call hard working! I'm sure it wasn't easy to reach the far corner of the bed but I see you managed to do it."

"Yup," he gulps as he bends down to take another look. Low and behold, he notices a small ball next to one of the legs. "Oh, I see I must have missed something," he says and he stretches out to pick it up. Once it is in his hand, he quickly puts the offending item into its proper place.

"Good for you, Ari," you say. "I see you are dedicated to finishing the tasks you set out to do. Perseverance is an important trait for a Jew to have."

Elisheva points to the beds. "These weren't easy to clean," she comments. "There was so much junk piled on top."

You examine the beds. "If I remember correctly," you say, "they were cluttered with books, papers and magazines. I see you put the books back on the shelf neatly, the papers back in the drawers and the magazines on top of your desk. That is what I call organization." She smiles gratefully. "That was always a strong point of yours," you continue. "I'm glad you're keeping it up. And I see that you worked hard to arrange the bedding. I'm sure it wasn't easy, it is so bulky."

Elisheva looks at the bed and notices that it is a bit lumpy in places and that the pillow looks as though it will fall off at any moment. "Yes, you're right," she admits. "The bedding is heavy and I just noticed that the pillow needs to be moved." She immediately pushes the pillow under the bedspread and smooths down the bed while you tuck the sheet under the mattress.

"Thank you for helping me," you say. "I see it takes two people to get the beds to have that 'just made look.'"

"Mommy, I cleaned this part of the room all by myself," Akiva says.

"Yes, it looks so neat, as though it were never messy," you say with a chuckle.

Akiva grins and points to the box containing miniature houses, stores and cars. "You'd never have known there was a whole town there if I hadn't told you, huh?"

"Nope," you reply. "Next time you ask me if you can play with that toy I won't hesitate to say yes, since I know that you can clean it up so thoroughly." He smiles with satisfaction.

You look under the drawers and start to pull out some papers. "Seems that these were missed in all the excitement. . . ."

"No, Mommy, don't," Penina cries out. "I hid them there so I could find them tomorrow."

"Oh, I understand," you say, "but let's put them in a place that is easy for you to locate but not visible to visitors. O.K.?" You show Penina that you are putting the papers in a folder in the top drawer of the desk. She seems content with the new arrangement.

"Kids, a job well done. I'm so proud of all of the *mitzvos* you have done tonight: *kibud av v'em, chesed* (helping one another) and *hakkaros hatov*, appreciating others. Now that we're finished, let's read that bedtime story I promised you. But first, it's time for pajamas."

With the kids sitting snugly in their pajamas, you start to read them a story. Then you hear your husband's key open the lock of the door. Mission accomplished!

৵§ Analysis of Effective Techniques

The preceding scenario was written to provide you with a small peek at effective delegation techniques for children. I hope that it illustrated the pros and cons of various methods that mothers use to coax their children to help them with household chores. Although some of the negative methods (such as yelling, threatening and name-calling) might have seem exaggerated in this chapter, to small children this is the way it sounds and feels — awful. It must be stressed, however, that children do not always show a willingness to help even when you employ every effective technique known to motherhood. Sometimes children are tired, irritable and simply won't cooperate. Hopefully, this will happen only occasionally. In general, if the proper techniques are utilized your children should respond in a positive manner.

The four major points stressed in this chapter were: 1) mother's attitude; 2) proper delegation techniques; 3) proper supervision; and 4) praise (effective communication). Children are very sensitive to their mother's feelings and moods. When a mother feels good physically and emotionally she is in a much better position to articulate her wishes in a clear and positive manner. This sets the tone for an effective interchange between mother and child.

Furthermore, when a mother is specific about exactly what job she wants the child to do and how she wants it done, the child is better able to carry out her request. Of course, no task should be delegated to a child who is incapable (physically or emotionally) of performing it. Consider each child's abilities and his current mood before assigning him a task. In addition, take into account his likes and dislikes.

Proper supervision is essential to achieving the desired results. If a child lacks the proper tools or the knowledge of how to do a job, it won't get done. And whether the child admits it or not, he will feel like a failure if he can't carry out the job you have assigned him. So make sure each child understands exactly how you expect the work to be accomplished.

Heartfelt praise is an essential part of the delegation process. It shows the child that you not only notice his efforts but appreciate them as well. Praise serves as essential feedback to teach a child what he is doing right. Be specific about his achievements. Global praise such as "you're terrific" is not as meaningful to him as comments about his specific accomplishments, such as, "Clothes hung up, books placed on shelves — you show attention to detail. Terrific." This gives him a concrete grasp of his successes and sets the stage for a repeat performance.

One important tool, given short shrift in this scenario, is that of charts. Charts can be a powerful way of inducing your children to help on a regular basis. Allow your creativity free reign. Charts needn't consist of simple lines and stars. They can be in the shape of a favorite game. They can be made of cork or cloth. Involve your children in the process.

But what can be offered as an incentive? The rewards for finishing their tasks don't have to be food treats. They can be educational, spiritual — you name it. As long as the child wants or needs it, it can work.

Most importantly, enjoy the time spent with your children. They do grow up!

Chapter Three

The Husband's Home Management Guide

Your wife is away and you're in charge. Now that you are on your own, you will gain a deeper appreciation of how much work it takes to keep a house running. Also, you'll be glad your wife left you this book. So have a seat and enjoy this chapter which was written especially for you.

❃   ❃   ❃

There are three basic areas that must be tended to in order to keep your household afloat: food, laundry and minimum maintenance.

❧ Food

Meals can be whipped up quickly only if there is food in the house. Take a look in the kitchen and jot down what's needed. The following list of basic necessities will help organize your thoughts. Call in an order to the local grocery store or, if possible, take the first opportunity and go off to the supermarket (a babysitter may be of help here).

■ *Perishables*

bread, butter, cheese, cold cuts, eggs, fruit, milk, rolls, vegetables

■ *Staples*

canned fruit, canned vegetables, flour, instant oatmeal or cream of wheat, jelly, ketchup, macaroni, mayonnaise, mustard, noodles, nosh (that extra incentive to prod your children into action), oil, packaged cereal, pepper, peanut butter, pancake mix, pancake syrup, rice, salad dressing, salt, soup mix, spaghetti, sugar, tomato sauce, tuna, vinegar

■ *Dry Goods*

aluminum foil, disposable diapers, laundry detergent, paper plates, paper towels, plastic bags, toilet paper

■ *Frozen Goods*

blintzes, chicken, fish, fish sticks, fruit juice, ice cream, pizza, meat, vegetables, any other convenience foods you all enjoy

With the cupboard and refrigerator properly stocked, mealtime panic will be minimized. It is wise to set mealtimes in advance. For example:

Breakfast — 7:00-7:30

Lunch — 12:30-1:30

Dinner 6:00 — 6:45.

Breakfast — cereal or eggs or pancakes

Lunch — sandwiches or cheese noodles, tuna salad or yogurt

Dinner — chicken or hamburger or roast meat or broiled fish

Side dishes (for lunch or dinner) — mashed potatoes, rice, or farfel

Vegetables — defrosted, canned, or fresh.

These are just suggestions; adjust times and menus to your family's needs. Please take note: start preparations about a half an hour before each meal, in order to prevent pandemonium and crying children. In a pinch, retreat to the local fast-food restaurant or bring home ready-made food.

To maintain order, a bit of kitchen maintenance will serve you well. Clean dishes, cutlery and table are the basics. Disposable dishes and cutlery are a great boon. If they are too costly, the following few hints will ease your way. Clear the table as soon as possible after the meal. Wash dishes, glasses and silverware frequently or place them in the dishwasher after each meal, running it at the end of the day. Of course, children can be enlisted to help with this task.

৶ Laundry

The trick is: wash and dry clothing *before* it is needed! Avoid last minute surprises, such as discovering that all the shirts are still at the bottom of the hamper as your ride pulls up or the school bus is on its way.

Separate laundry into whites, light colors, and coloreds, and wash accordingly (unless you prefer pink shirts and pants coated with lint). Whites are washed with hot water, lights with warm water, darks with cool water. Delicates items can be hand washed, or machine laundered on the delicate cycle. Do a separate load of towels and rags, using hot or warm water.

Before doing a wash, read the instructions on your laundry detergent, because too little soap leaves the clothing dingy and too much will strain the washing machine. To minimize ironing, tumble dry, remove immediately and hang. If you prefer, clothing can be taken out of the washing machine before the spin cycle and hung on a hanger; just smooth out the wrinkles and press down the collars. Clean children's laundry can be sorted into baskets and given to each child to put away.

✍ Morning Routine

Set your alarm to ring several minutes earlier than planned. When rushing to get everyone out in the morning, the situation can become tense. Give yourself leeway. Your cheerful manner as you dress and feed the children will start their day right.

Mornings proceed more smoothly if clothing and lunches are prepared the night before. *Kippot, tzitzis,* socks and shoes should all be placed in a central location to avoid your having to rummage through closets and under beds for these evanescent items. If it is impractical to prepare lunch boxes at night, at least do the groundwork. Clear kitchen counters and be sure to have the necessary ingredients on hand, including: the sandwich fixings, bread, clean knives and spoons, plastic bags or aluminum foil and lunch bags.

Can you hire a baby sitter or ask a neighbor to watch the children when you *daven shacharis?* Confirm arrangements the day before, or you may be unable to *daven* with a *minyan*.

✍ Dinner and Bedtime Routine

Allow plenty of time for this. It always takes longer than you think. Be wary about rushing children into bed. The more you hurry, the hungrier and thirstier they will be, requesting one more drink, one more piece of fruit, one more. . .

Plan a quiet time for the hour preceding their sleep. (Contrary to what you might think, an exercise session before bed will make them *more* energetic not less.) A book to read, a favorite tape, a few minutes of quiet talk, all relax little bodies after a busy day. Avoid middle-of-the-night searches — keep bottles, pacifiers, and special cuddly toys in an easily accessible place. And do not forget to DIAPER THE BABY!

ᴇᷟ Household Maintenance

At some point in the day, or after the children are asleep, allow time for basic maintenance. This will include: putting away clothing, picking up items from the floor (try to get children to pick up toys after playing or before bedtime), clearing off tables and counters, emptying ashtrays and replacing toilet paper. You may also want to include planning meals, doing laundry and washing dishes. As you straighten up in each room, note areas in need of sweeping or vaccuming. Neglected dirt sets in deeply and can become grueling work, so don't forget this last, finishing touch.

An ounce of prevention will go a long way. Teach children to wipe off their shoes before entering the house. Clean spills as they occur. Encourage the little ones to wear bibs. Don't let kids' play areas get out of hand. Make it a rule that children must put back toys before they go on to another activity.

ᴇᷟ Shabbos

If you are still waiting for a Shabbos invitation you might want to drop a hint; friends and neighbors probably don't realize that your wife is away. Once you're invited be sure to mention to the hostess any special dietary restrictions you or your children may have. If you will be sleeping out, pack the overnight bag on Thursday. Be sure to include two changes of clothing for every person. Don't forget tissues, diapers, toys, pacifiers, baby bottles and so forth. Mark down last-minute items which can only be packed on Friday — don't forget your *tallis*!

If you and the children will be spending Shabbos at home, make a list of all the essentials: grape juice, six challahs, fish, chicken, kugel, tzimmes, cholent, salads, cake and fruit. If ordering from a take-out shop, clarify in advance the store's deadline for Shabbos orders or you may be left empty-handed. And if that's exactly where you are now, don't despair. Turn to page 94 in our Meal Management chapter, where you will find easy-to-prepare Shabbos meals.

Chapter Four

Beating the Laundry Blues
... and Whites and ...

I've often wondered what it is about laundry that makes most housewives feel so overwhelmed. After all, we live in the automated age of washing machines, dryers and steam irons. All we have to do is sort it, throw it in and let the machines do the rest.

But there is a catch. Laundry is more than washing and drying clothes, which is the easy part. It's an entire process that starts with buying clothes wisely, then caring for them, collecting them from forgotten corners, treating them for stains, soaking, washing, drying them, and then there's sorting, ironing, folding and returning them to their rightful place before they end up back on the floor in a crumpled mess. The laundry process isn't static either. It grows with the family. Once you realize what you're dealing with, you are on the way to conquering the laundry blues. . .and whites and greens and stains. . .

Make laundry time a breeze by making the best choices about your clothes and the way you handle them. Avoid buying delicate clothes that are hand washable only, or fabrics which require ironing. Avoid buying dresses in dark colors with white cuffs, as the cuffs tend to turn gray quickly. High quality plaid and patterned outfits are better buys because they tend to show less dirt and they are easily washed and cared for. This is particularly important if you're handing down clothing. Use vinegar in the rinse water or use products made specifically to keep colors bright, which also contributes to the longevity of your clothing.

In addition to the type of clothing you choose, the amount you own is another important variable in the laundry equation. If your closets and drawers are large enough, you may prefer to buy enough clothing for every family member to wear the entire week. The advantage here is that you have to wash clothing only once a week because you have plenty in stock. If you have more than four children you may find that a three-day supply is more than adequate, as laundry needs to be done at least two or three times a week anyway. Owning less clothing per child cuts down on the cost of clothing, clutter and the need for storage space. Clothes that aren't being used at the present time shouldn't be stored in prime storage space. Get rid of any gifts or hand-me-downs that are impractical or disliked. They will fill your drawers like weeds and be just as useful. If your child refuses to wear an outfit that is in good condition, or if it doesn't fit him but might be appropriate for another child, then you should store it if you have the storage space.

◄§ Prevention

There is another piece of information which is essential to the successful completion of the laundry puzzle. If you guessed "prevention," you are right. I'm referring to aprons for women and bibs for children. You don't have to wear an apron all day (although there are women who do), neither must your child always wear a bib, but when you are using bleach, involved in heavy cleaning or dirty work or feeding your children, wear an apron or housecoat because it will save your clothing from acquiring permanent stains. Children should also wear a protective bib or other covering when they eat or get involved in messy projects such as painting or playing with mud.

Once clothing or tableclothes become stained, treat the stain as quickly as possible. Commercial stain removers such as Spray and Wash, Clorox, or Off, work well on chocolate, beets, oil stains, as well as others. To use, wash off any encrusted food, then spray on the stain remover and rub a generous amount in, letting it penetrate for a few minutes, then scrub a bit. Another option is to make a paste out of any heavy duty laundry detergent, rub it on the stain, leave it overnight and wash out the next morning. For most fruit stains or blood stains it is best to pour cold water on them immediately. Hot water often sets these stains, making it hard to remove them. Gum poses a special challenge. The old trick, ice, works well on large pieces, but I've found "Freon Freeze" (available in most drugstores) is faster and cleaner to work with. Hairspray takes out ink stains. Spray and leave for a few minutes and then scrub out. For candle wax put two paper towels on either side of the fabric and iron with a hot iron. The wax will melt off and be absorbed onto the paper towel. If a stain is left, then treat in the above manner and wash. Children's clothing or work clothing which is very dirty but not really stained requires pre-soaking with a non-chlorine bleach.

◄§ Laundry Location

Before you can wash dirty laundry it must be gathered and put in its proper place. So keep laundry bins in convenient places. A client of mine was frantic because her children never put their dirty laundry in the hampers. One was located in the bathroom, and it was often full and far from the children's sight (and memory). Because it was often full, the children didn't want to add more to it, and the mother always felt that the laundry was overflowing (because it was!) The other hamper in the laundry room was only convenient for dirty kitchen towels. After the woman placed a hamper in each of the two children's rooms, the problem was solved.

There could be three hampers in the bathroom if you have space — one for whites, one for colors and one for towels and sheets. This makes it easy to determine when you have a full load. Or you can place a hamper in every bedroom and bathroom, take each one to the laundry room on a regular basis, and sort their contents into three hampers (whites, colors, towels and sheets). If you have a built in laundry chute, you may try to train your household members to use it.

And speaking of convenient placement, if I had my choice I'd build a laundry room with proper lighting and large enough to house a washing machine, dryer, iron and ironing board, wash lines, and a special shelf for detergents, softener and other laundry products. While some of us might be lucky enough to enjoy this arrangement, many apartment dwellers have their washing machines in the bathroom and their dryers in another area. In this case, develop your own system to prevent too much running back and forth. Keep the laundry detergent and any other needed items near the washing machine and dryer.

The following are a few sample laundry schedules:

◄§ Laundry Schedules

Once a Week

Laundry day comes once a week but you will have to do it morning till evening. This system works well for families with three children or less and is very helpful for women who work full-time. It requires owning both a washer and a dryer. The advantage is obvious — work hard one day but forget about it the rest of the week. This is also the most convenient method if you have to use a laundromat.

Two or Three Times a Week

This system works for women who can't finish all the laundry in one day but don't want to do it every day. For those who don't have enough laundry to do full loads every day, this schedule saves time and energy. A variation of this system is to wash and dry laundry one day and put it away the next day.

Every Day except Friday (and Shabbos)

This system is suitable for large families since there are at least one to two full loads of wash every day. Whatever schedule you choose, never do laundry on Friday and make sure the Shabbos clothing is ready early in the week. You might assign one day for whites, one for colors and another for sheets and towels.

⊷ Ironing and Putting Away

What happens to your clothing once it is washed and dried? Does it get thrown into one large laundry basket which eventually overflows? One client of mine used to dump all her laundry into a crib which was not being used. The problem was, it stayed there. Whenever she needed something she pulled it out of the crib. While this wasn't terrible for underclothing, her little boy's pants and husband's shirts were wrinkled beyond recognition. To prevent this, take these items of clothing out of the dryer as soon as they are dry, straighten out each article and hang it up so you won't have to iron it. The rest of the dry clothing can be put in the laundry basket. Personally, I try to avoid ironing. That's why all boys' and men's shirts in my house are permanent press, as are the tablecloths.

As some husbands tend to be particular about their shirts and some women just enjoy that crisp look, it is important to make the task of ironing convenient. When you do iron, make sure the ironing board is at a height which is comfortable for you. Provide yourself with proper lighting along with spray starch, hangers and a place to put unironed as well as ironed items. Unless your ironing board is always set up and ready to use, it saves precious minutes to iron a large number of articles at once rather than one piece at a time.

Like many in Israel, if you do not have a dryer, take pants, shirts and skirts out of the washing machine while they are dripping wet — before the spin cycle. Smooth them out with your hands and hang them on the laundry line with clothespins or suspended from hangers. (The latter saves you a step in the process, as you can hang them straight in the closet). This process usually "irons" these articles sufficiently; at most, they will need only a light touch up.

Once all the laundry is washed and dried, take a moment to feel good about this accomplishment. There is still more work ahead of you. The clothing must be sorted and put away for the job to be truly finished. Here are some ways to accomplish this task (choose one). When you take clothing off of the line or out of the dryer you will put it into:

1. a basket for each member of the family, who is responsible for folding and putting away his own laundry. (It can be left in the laundry room or brought to a central location.)

2. a basket for each room.
   a. you sort and fold and put away the contents of each basket in each room.
   b. one child sorts and folds and puts away each item.
   c. each child finds his own clothing and then folds and puts away each item.

3. One big pile of clothing is left in a central place, like the living room or an out of the way location, and then it is sorted, folded and put away.

If your household help does the laundry, your children sort the clothing, or you have similar clothing of different sizes (white boys' shirts, sizes 3, 5, and 7) make sure to institute a labeling system. This could be a number or a colored dot on each item of clothing with a matching symbol on the children's drawer or shelf.

If you are in a bind, keep in mind that most cities have laundry services. Although these may be expensive on a regular basis, they might provide the perfect solution if your washing machine breaks down, you become ill, or just sick of laundry and need a break.

And when you've finished the laundry for today and turn around to find the hamper already full again, remember this sign which I saw above my friend's washing machine:

לֹא עָלֶיךָ הַמְלָאכָה לִגְמוֹר וְלֹא אַתָּה בֶּן חוֹרִין לְהִבָּטֵל מִמֶּנּוּ

It's not up to you to finish all the work, but you're not free to ignore it either.

Chapter Five

How to Live Anywhere in a Small Apartment on a Budget
(With Israeli Housekeeping Hints)

✑ Making the Most of Close Quarters

Dear Chaya and Nechama,

Living in Israel had always been a dream for me, the kind you wait to fulfill until you're at least sixty. But sooner than I imagined, this dream became a reality and I found myself packing up our household and boarding a flight. I'm still trying to find an apartment with a bedroom bigger than our beds, a kitchen big enough for our American refrigerator and oven, and enough light to make my way down the hall. Any help you can offer would be appreciated.

Dear Newcomer,

Whether it be in an apartment in Jerusalem or in Brooklyn, living in close quarters is always a challenge. A real estate agent can help you find a bigger place and an architect can suggest ways to move interior walls. All we can offer you are some guidelines for transforming small, crowded interiors into roomy, comfortable dwellings where every inch counts.

Small rooms can be versatile and appealing if you know how to make the most of them. Using color and light you can create the illusion of space. Applying the following rules, you can actually color your rooms larger: pale colors recede, bold colors advance, contrasting colors emphasize, and closely blended colors conceal. Therefore, if you want to make your living room appear larger, choose a pale color scheme. For example, cream-colored walls, beige furniture and a light brown carpet will do the trick. Add bright-colored accent pieces to keep the room from looking drab and dull.

Furniture will seem to blend into the wall if both are a similar color. Thus, in a small off-white kitchen, an off-white table flush against the wall will give the kitchen a more spacious appearance. Large, bright prints will make furnishings look bigger and bulkier; avoid them. Instead use fine prints and delicate patterns which will add color and design without detracting from the size of the room.

Creative use of light will also give the illusion of space. Because dark corners tend to shrink a room, install lamps or light fixtures in strategic locations to eliminate darkness. In a dark room which doesn't get enough sun consider a halogen lamp, whose light most simulates sunlight. Fluorescent light fixtures also come in an array of warmer and cooler tones.

Grand illusions with small and medium-sized mirrors can also enhance small rooms and especially halls. Place the mirror opposite a window or pretty picture to reflect a pleasant sight. A mirror which reflects a white wall will not add much to the room's aesthetics.

In addition to color and light, the size and placement of furniture make a big difference in determining whether your room will appear crowded or spacious. Consider carefully the traffic lanes in each room when arranging your furniture. Bumping into a chair each time you pass through the living room can be quite a frustrating experience. If possible, place furniture against the walls to provide ample space in the middle of the room. The entrance to each room should be clear of protruding chair legs, table tops and footstools. Make sure the edges of your rugs are not situated in such a way as to cause people to trip over them; if so, put the ends under furniture.

Select small-scale furnishings for a small apartment. Avoid heavy or bulky pieces which take up too much area. Look for slender, sleeker furniture to save on floor space.

For maximum efficiency put your rooms to double work; just make sure the functions don't overlap. For example, if your living room doubles as a bedroom, it should not be used by someone who goes to bed at seven o'clock, because you won't be able to receive guests at night, unless you can find another room for this purpose. Sometimes, a kitchen can serve nicely for receiving guests or just relaxing, if it is spacious enough. Your bedroom can double as your office. With a desk and typewriter in the corner of the room, you can work mornings and evenings without interfering with your baby's nap in the afternoon.

Don't overlook double-duty furniture. Rather than having two children's beds side by side, consider a pullout bed or a bunk bed. There are even attractive daybeds which look like couches yet conceal one or two beds underneath. A couch that opens into a bed, a chest which serves as a bench, or a bookcase which conceals a pullout desk are just a few examples of furniture which can enhance the capabilities of your home.

Eliminate unnecessary furniture and accessories. Instead of standing a plant on a table consider placing the plant in a hanging fixture. Instead of placing knicknacks all around the room, gather them together on one shelf where they won't take up much needed space. This also applies to clothing, kitchen gadgets and anything else that takes up valuable storage space. (For more information on de-cluttering see "Goodbye Clutter" page 81.)

Look for storage opportunities in every room. Say no to Aunt Edith's "antique" corner table which stands on three legs. Instead, install a corner table housing a cabinet underneath. Other places to look for space are next to your couch or reclining chair, on top of cabinets, underneath beds and behind headboards. There are many new and attractive storage accessories available at discount stores and specialty shops. In Israel, Keter outlets and Hamashbir Department Stores carry a complete line of storage containers.

When seeking out storage opportunities make sure to use prime space only for frequently used items and hard-to-reach space for off-season items. Prime space refers to any shelf, cabinet or hanging rod which you can reach easily. Any shelf or cabinet which you can reach only with the aid of a stool is non-prime space and should be used for items you require less than once a month. (See page 69 for a more detailed description of prime space.)

With these guidelines, you should be able to make the most of your rooms in a small apartment.

☙ Budgeting

Dear Chaya and Nechama,

When I was first married I always seemed to have enough money for my needs. Helpful relatives pitched in for things I couldn't afford. Now my family is growing, prices are rising and our income just isn't keeping up with the demands. I dread the thought of living under a tight budget where I have to write down every single purchase, collect coupons and shop only after I've compared prices in every store in my area. Is there a better way?

Dear Budget Resistant,

Budgeting needn't be a dreaded task. It can be enjoyable and rewarding if performed in a realistic manner fitting your lifestyle. The following is a basic budget outline:

1. Add up total monthly income including that of husband, wife, along with any other sources.
2. Make a list of expenses (for example, rent or mortgage payments, food, utility bills, insurance premiums, medical bills, repairs, clothing, transportation, savings, Shabbos and Yom Tov expenses, schooling, domestic help, mistakes, and so on).
3. Separate fixed expenses from flexible expenses. Fixed expenses are those expenses which you must meet, such as debt repayments (loans or installment payments) insurance premiums, rent or mortgage, education, taxes and *ma'aser*. Add up your fixed expenses and subtract from total income.
4. Now compute your flexible expenses. Flexible expenses are regularly occurring expenses whose amounts vary. They include: car, clothing, food, utilities and the like. These vary based on season and habit. For instance, most people's food bills increase for Yom Tov and their gas and electric bill is higher in the winter than in the summer. You can choose to be more energy conscious thereby lowering utility bills. Or you can decide to ride in a carpool rather than drive to work everyday. Approximate the amounts you spend on each of these items.
5. Check the amounts you are spending on flexible expenses over the next three months by recording outlays or saving bills in a notebook designed for this purpose.
6. Pay attention to regularly occurring "unexpected" expenses, such as orthodontist bills, special tutoring for your children, and so on. Some "extra expense" always crops up when you have a family. Remember to allot "extra money" for flexible expenses such as these.

7. What you have left is money for savings, household purchases and travel. Decide how much you want to save and how to save it. Do you want to set aside money every month in a savings account? Do you want to set aside money in a household safe towards the purchase of a new couch?
8. Try to keep a small cushion of funding for emergencies.
9. Statistically speaking, many people find the following system of allotting funds useful:

    30% — food
    20% — rent or mortgage
    20% — education, transportation, repairs
    15% — utilities
    15% — clothing

If you find that you overspend, try some of these ideas: Shop by phone for groceries, fruits and vegetables to help you crack down on impulse buying. When you go shopping bring with you just enough cash to buy what is written on your shopping list. Don't carry a checkbook or charge card, which makes it easier to splurge on non-essential items. But be careful to avoid the mistake of cutting back on small items which carry emotional weight. If you enjoy eating butter on toast, don't buy margarine because it is less expensive. If you follow this approach, it will backfire, bringing down your morale and making it more difficult to resist a spending spree later. Better to turn off lights when they're not in use or to cut down on the use of other utilities to reduce spending. These measures won't make you feel destitute, just budget conscious.

ᴥᶳ Israeli Cleaning

Dear Chaya and Nechama,

My mother taught me the basics of keeping house. I learned how to dust with Lemon Pledge, vacuum the carpets and wipe the counters and table tops. Laundry was a breeze with All Temperature Cheer and our Sears push-button washing machine.

Just sort the laundry and press the right button; everything was clearly marked.

Unfortunately, here in Israel, my housekeeping knowledge falls dreadfully short when faced with formica closets, stone floors and a small Israeli washing machine. I'm despairing quickly. . .

Dear Despairing,

Don't give up hope. Here are some cleaning guidelines culled from expert Israeli *balabustas*, including the never-before-published *sponga* secret traditionally handed down from generation to generation.

Biomat, Pisga or Sod are a few of the Israeli laundry detergent favorites which can be used in all temperatures. Add Kleen or Ran whiteners, which are non-chlorine bleaches, to light-colored and white loads to keep clothes looking fresh and new. A fabric softener, such as Badin or Pisga, added during the last rinse of a cycle, will make your clothes come out smelling fresher; in addition, they will dry softer. If you dry towels on a clothesline, then fabric softener must be used so they don't dry as hard as a rock.

If you own an Israeli or European washing machine: wash whites on cycle 1 at 60-80 degrees, light-colored shirts and skirts on cycle 2 at 60 degrees, light to medium colored clothes on cycle 3 at 45-50 degrees, towels on cycle 3 at 50 degrees, and darks on cycle 4 at 30 degrees.

Formica surfaces are best cleaned with an all-purpose cleaner, such as Fantastik, mixed with water. It should be sprayed on, left to soak for a minute and then wiped off. Bleach or ammonia will remove the lamination and cause the surface to dull.

To clean sinks and bathtubs use Trick, Sano or any other non-scratching disinfectant powder, which will clean thoroughly and leave a shiny finish.

Kitchen and bathroom tiles can be cleaned with a solution of ammonia and water in a spray bottle. Either wipe clean or use a squeegee stick. Leave a small squeegee in the shower and bathtub to wipe down tiles after each use. If you can't tolerate the smell of ammonia then use Sano-Kleer, Gottlein or Windowlane which come in handy spray bottles. The same cleaning agents can be used to clean windows as well, but use a newspaper to wipe up the cleanser.

Stainless steel and ceramic sinks can be washed down with hot water and a cleanser such as Ajax, Comet or Sano. Bleach can be used on most white ceramic kitchen sinks and helps prevent mold build up.

Now here it is, the secret to getting stone floors and marble counter tops really clean: use hot soapy water, then remove it completely with a good squeegee stick. This means that to clean marble counters you follow this method: Remove all items from the counter. Pour a solution of Fantastik and water onto the counter top. Let it soak for a minute; scrub with Scotchbrite only if necessary. Then squeegee all soapy water into the sink. Next, pour hot water over the counter and squeegee off for a mirrorlike shine. Dry any streaks with a clean rag.

For a stone or marble floor: You don't have to sweep first if you employ this method. Remove all objects from floor. Pour Fantastik diluted with water on floor and spread with a straw broom (a witch's broom), scrubbing when necessary. Discovering the right amount of water to cover the floor without flooding the house will take a few tries. Then use a squeegee stick to push the water into the drainpipe. (If your pipe is clogged, non-existent, or drains onto your neighbor's porch, use less water and squeegee into one spot in the room. Then sweep water into dustpan and pour into a bucket.) Make sure to remove as much dirty water as possible. Then wipe the floor with a rag dampened with clean hot water. Rinse the rag once it becomes soiled. I clean the floor of a five-room apartment in one-and-a-half hours and my neighbors want to know who my "Israeli" cleaning woman is.

Chapter Six

Tips for Large Families: Daily Challenges and Scheduling

Bracha entered the large room hesitantly as she searched the crowd for her friend Esther. Music was playing softly in the background. She recognized a few familiar faces, among them Sheindy. Was she expecting again? Bracha made a quick mental count; she realized Sheindy had nine at home, yet she still looked so young and energetic. Absorbed in her thoughts, she didn't notice Esther standing next to two empty seats and waving in her direction. "I'm glad you could make it," Esther said as Bracha approached.

"I really needed the night off," Bracha admitted. "With five children under the age of six, I sometimes feel as if my brain has stopped functioning between 'wash your hands' and 'make a brachah'. Where did all those years of learning chumash with commentary go? I'm so tired, I hope tonight's speaker isn't too theoretical or long-winded, or I won't be able to follow," she said as she sat down to join the other women seated around the large table in the center of the room. Everyone at the table laughed.

Adelle whispered to Bracha, "I know how you feel. After I had my triplets, I really needed a lot of inspiration, but in bite-sized pieces. I made every effort to attend a shiur at least once a week."

"You go to shiurim?" Shani asked. "I find it too difficult to arrange for baby sitters, and the children usually don't sleep as well when I'm out. I prefer to get my inspiration from tapes."

"I wouldn't see an adult face if I didn't go out of my house to attend a shiur," Adelle replied.

Bracha nodded in understanding and added, "At this stage of my life I just need time for myself."

"Right," Esther agreed. "That's why I cuddle up with a book every night before I go to sleep.

"I'll tell you what keeps me going," Julie said enthusiastically. "Taking care of myself by eating well and exercising regularly does the trick. After my weekly exercise class I return home refreshed and ready to work. Hindy and I have been discussing going swimming, too. Sheindy told me that's what helps her stay so fit."

Yocheved, who had been sitting quietly, finally spoke up. The first among her friends to marry, she already had a daughter of marriageable age. She had a very large family and devoted all of her time to her house and children. Her classmates had assumed that she would pursue a career since, as a student, she had excellent grades, high test scores and a strong desire to achieve. Instead she channeled all of her talents and energy into her home. "Listening to you, you'd think there was no joy in raising children and building a Jewish home," Yocheved said. "Every day I feel the *brachah* of running a house filled with *chesed* and *mitzvos*. When I cook and serve food to my children, I remember that it is to enable them to serve Hashem. When I do laundry, I have in mind how clean and fresh they will feel when they learn Torah. When I take care of my babies, I think about how helpless they are. In relation to Hashem, we too are helpless, so caring for my infants provides me with a lesson in *emunah* and *bitachon*. All day long I'm performing acts of *chesed*, which is how I can emulate Hashem. As I cook for Shabbos I say, *le'kavod Shabbos kodesh*. While washing dishes I *daven* to Hashem to give me the energy to take care of the little ones and to help my older ones find a good *shidduch*. And it goes without saying that I get infinite joy out of watching my children develop from tiny infants into capable adults. There are endless opportunities for inspiration and spirituality right in front of our eyes if we take the time to look for them."

All those gathered listened attentively to Yocheved's words. When she finished, she sat back and smiled at the group of women. Esther broke the silence. "I'm impressed," she said. "It seems that you have been able to view your daily existence on a high spiritual level, even without constant outside inspiration. Clearly, we all agree on the need to keep ourselves on track and happy with our own unique mission in life. I wonder what tonight's 'expert' is going to say about this particular point."

"I'm waiting for some great magic tricks to make my dishes disappear into the cabinets," Julie said with a smirk.

The music stopped and Mrs. Shoenberg stood up at the front of the room to speak. "Ladies, I'm so glad you could all make it this evening," she said. "Tonight our special guest speaker is a household management consultant. She and her partner started a business called Creative Options to assist religious women with running their homes."

I stood up next to the hostess. "When Mrs. Shoenberg called and asked me to speak about how to manage with a growing family, I envisioned a supermarket-sized parking lot filled with station wagons," I began. "You see, having grown up in suburbia, I remember the station wagon being the symbol of the large family. Many women came to expect that a station wagon would replace their compact after the birth of their fourth child. But recently, the van has become the preferred choice of transportation. I presume this indicates that with even larger families, station wagons aren't large enough to accommodate everyone." I'd caught my audience's attention and gotten a few knowing smiles.

"But those of us who are blessed with larger families know that outgrowing our cars is one of the simpler problems we contend with. It's the daily challenges — the cooking, the care of children, the endless laundry — that demand our attention and sap our strength. The larger the family, the more important organization becomes. In order to accomplish all the technical jobs, such as cleaning and cooking, as well as to devote time to our children, we must be organized in terms of housework, time, space and so forth.

"Whereas with a small family you can afford to waste a morning or an afternoon, with a larger brood the lost time can have serious negative consequences. There is a constant need for considering how to make the best use of your time and energy. For example, if I decide to cook from scratch every day, thus ensuring a fresh meal, then I am also deciding to spend less time doing something else, such as reading to my toddler or taking my baby for a walk. If I opt to use paper plates, which add to my expenses, I have also opted to devote more time to the children or to other housework. Do I plan that one night a week I will go out to a *shiur* or do I stay home and serve my older children supper? Do I hire household help or will I clean the house by myself and save my money for something else? And my decision doesn't affect just one person — it affects seven people or more.

"How will my children spend their time? Will my little ones go to play group or stay at home with me? Will my children go to piano lessons, art classes or friends' homes? The constant decision-making takes time. Therefore, plan ahead and write down your arrangements in a schedule, thereby leaving you time for more important decisions. As a good friend of mine with nine children, *bli ayin hara,* always says, 'It is a big *chesed* on Hashem's part that all our children aren't born at the same time. Instead, we have time to grow along with our increasing responsibilities.'

"Of course, not every large family is the same, and what works for you will depend on your particular situation. A family with eight children under the age of ten is very different from a family with eight under the age of eighteen, or a family of all boys or two sets of twins. Finances, temperaments and needs also differ.

"Therefore, I cannot discuss every issue pertinent to your individual situations, but I'd like to touch upon those which are crucial to the smooth functioning of large families."

At this point most of the women were sitting forward, listening carefully, and others had pulled out pens and notebooks. I went on.

"Let us start with meal planning. To make sizable quantities of food, large pots and storage containers are essential. Some women cook twice a week, doubling each portion as they cook (see chapter on meal management page 88). But often it is easier to cook simple meals every day. Either way it is important to have recipes that can be made in large quantities.

If your oldest isn't old enough to help, you might opt to rely on frozen and canned vegetables, soups and ready-made challah and baked goods. Or you might cut vegetables into sticks instead of making salads. If you have older children who enjoy baking and cooking, then leave the meal preparation to them. One friend of mine, a mother of small children, makes challah and cookie dough every Thursday. In the afternoon her 2, 4, 6 and 8 year olds are busy rolling out cookies and making challahs. Some women wouldn't allow this because of the mess; other women wouldn't mind.

Whether you prefer to rely on convenience items or prepare everything from scratch, the most important consideration is to have meals on the table at mealtime and still find opportunities to take care of other business.

"For hassle-free meal preparation you need to keep a large stock of food supplies on hand. Most large families benefit from buying non-perishable products in bulk once a month. Look for wholesale outlets that sell these items at a discount. Some of these issue membership cards and allow only a specific clientele to join, but don't let these requirements deter you from investigating membership.

"Perishable items require more shopping time because they are bought more frequently. Perhaps delegate this task to an older child or arrange for your husband to go shopping on his way home from shul. If this isn't feasible, then arrange to buy once a week (at a time when the store is the least crowded) and keep extra purchases of bread in the freezer. Some shops will take phone orders and deliver to your home.

"As food preparation and cooking leave memorable traces, in the form of dishes and pots, you can decide ahead of time how you will tackle them. Will you wash up after each meal or stack your utensils, cleaning them at the end of the day? Remember that paper plates and cups can cut down dramatically on dish washing. If you have a dishwasher, you may want to scrape or rinse the dishes after each meal, putting them in the dishwasher and running it when it is full.

"Now let's talk about those daily loads of laundry we all contend with. First, I will mention that there is no way out of it until someone invents disposable clothing! Diaper services and disposable diapers have done a lot to lighten the burden. Choose the laundry system that works best for you in keeping clean clothes available. (See Chapter 4 Beating the Laundry Blues page 154). Decide when laundry will be done and who will wash, dry and put away clothes. Consult older children when buying their clothes so that they will be more willing to wear and take care of them. Did you know that even a five year old can be taught to fold and put away his own clean clothing? Enlist your children's help and the chore of laundry will become less burdensome.

"With all household tasks, delegation is the way to keep the ship sailing smoothly. Many women fear that giving their children too much responsibility will have negative repercussions. This is a valid concern, to which I usually respond that in a large family there are usually enough helpers available to keep jobs evenly distributed. When you delegate work, take into consideration your child's own preferences. Does she have a special way with the toddler? Or does she prefer to go food shopping? Does he have school exams this week, or some other activity that will interfere with his ability to take on household tasks? Of course, with a house full of small children you cannot expect the same amount of help. However, they can pick up their own toys, put laundry in the hamper and carry objects from one room to another.

"In addition to dishes and laundry, daily maintenance includes making the beds and straightening up (putting away the stray clutter found on the floors and counter tops in each room). What will be included in your daily maintenance routine, and will you delegate any of the tasks to your children or to outside help? When will each job be accomplished? Do you prefer to do housework in the morning, the evening, or both? You have many options available to you. Women who hold down a job will be more limited and will need outside help as well.

"It is important to create a daily schedule and to stick to it. Decide in advance the best way to get all the children up, dressed, fed and to school on time. Will the younger ones stay at home or attend preschool? How will you manage dinner and bedtime routines in the smoothest manner possible? Once you have answered these questions you are on your way to creating a schedule that will work for you.

Many women, especially working mothers, find that the only way to get out of the house on time in the morning is by waking up before their children do and getting dressed, *davening* and straightening up the house or preparing breakfast. Then they wake up the children. Some women have difficulty getting up before their children do, so they prepare as much as is possible the night before. They lay out the clothing, make the sandwiches, set the table for breakfast and do whatever else needs to be done.

In homes with older children, many use the pairing method. They assign an older child to a younger one, to help him get dressed and make his bed. Some families use the team method to ensure order. All those in the same room constitute a team and are responsible for making the beds, cleaning the room and seeing to it that everyone is dressed and ready for school on time. Other families prefer to rotate the clean-up assignment on a weekly basis. A hanging chart is used to remind the children of their responsibilities.

"Another common scheduling problem in large families arises with mealtimes. How do you prepare and serve lunch and dinner when everyone comes home from school at a different time? It is conceivable that a woman can enter the kitchen at eight o'clock in the morning and not leave it until eight o'clock in the evening! Between making, serving and cleaning up from breakfast, lunch and dinner for many youngsters with clashing schedules, a woman could easily find herself in such a situation. Two solutions are: divide each meal into two rounds or provide healthy snacks between each set mealtime. If it isn't possible to have family meals with all present, take heart, Shabbos comes once a week.

"When will you spend quality time with your children and how will you occupy your children when you are busy? Some mothers set aside specific times of the day to spend with their children. For example, two o'clock until five o'clock is spent playing and doing homework with the younger children and seven o'clock until nine o'clock is devoted to the older children. Some women even share an hour of swimming or attend *shiurim* on a regular basis with their older daughters. Other mothers prefer giving their children activities to do by themselves while they attend to light housework and make themselves available for questions and interruptions. There are women who allow their children to follow them along with a play broom and other toys as they work. Extracurricular activities, visiting a friend or outdoor play can also be planned into a child's schedule. The trick is to decide that day's activities in advance before they come to you with the universal cry, 'We're bored. There's nothing to do!' Usually, at that stage of the game, almost anything you suggest will be rejected.

"Some mothers find that they are so busy keeping the ship afloat that the time they can devote to each child consists of only a few minutes when the child comes home from school and a few minutes before bedtime. Keep in mind that those are crucial moments and, if handled correctly, your warmth and love will be felt and appreciated. The actual amount of time you spend with your children and their specific schedules will be determined by their age, personality and needs. Children differ and so will their needs to: visit with friends, romp outdoors, play indoors, have quiet time, color or read, be with Mommy.

"How do you use your evenings? Do you finish housework or do you take the time to attend a *shiur*, talk on the phone or read a book? Perhaps you share the evenings with your husband and eldest son when he returns from yeshivah. If you devote them to housework and older children, then you might give yourself the mornings to take care of your own needs."

✎§ Expect the Unexpected

I paused for a moment and looked around the room before going on. "Although I've spent so much time describing scheduling and organization, I know I've made it all sound like smooth sailing. It would only be fair to mention that anyone with a large family knows that despite her hard work and good intentions some emergency is bound to crop up and destroy her carefully laid plans. An urgent errand, doctor's appointment, last-minute teacher's meeting or some other emergency are just some of the possible occurrences that can disrupt your schedule. So remember this rule, made especially for mothers of large families: EXPECT THE UNEXPECTED. Leave at least one morning or one afternoon a week for unscheduled errands and doctors' appointments or to catch up after an unexpected event. Try not to overbook each day, so that if a child becomes ill, or something important pops up, you will be able to fit the additional activity into your schedule.

"It is likewise helpful to consider in advance a possible course of action in the event of an emergency. For example, if it is *erev Shabbos* and your child is running a high temperature, call the doctor before Shabbos and discuss all of the possible consequences of the illness. If you need prompt medical attention, what procedure will you follow? What will happen if your child is sick and you have to go to work? Do you have a baby sitter or a relative to fill in at home, or can you take a leave of absence? What will happen if you don't feel well and you must stay in bed? Plan now while you can think clearly and there is no pressure.

"I recommend keeping a notebook for your husband and older children that contains specific instructions and phone numbers of baby sitters, relatives and neighbors to be contacted in case of an emergency. Make a list of stores that can deliver food by phone order. Record the items that are bought in these stores, along with their names, phone numbers and addresses. In addition, include a basic schedule or any pertinent information such as: Shuli has piano lessons every Monday at 4:00 p.m with Mrs. Parker, 555-6140, Yitzchak receives vitamins every morning, which are on the top shelf of the refrigerator."

I stopped talking to let the women in the audience write down any important information they would include in such a notebook. As I looked around the room my heart was full of admiration for these women who worked so hard and accepted their responsibilites with such love and devotion.

"O.K. ladies, I would like to finish the lecture for tonight with a reminder," I said in a loud, clear voice. "Even with all of the helpful suggestions we have mentioned, there will be times when nothing you do will seem to go the way you intended it to. There will be times when all of your plans will be sabotaged, and you will look around at the piles of dishes and laundry and wonder what went wrong. But don't let that little voice of despair fool you. Nothing is wrong. You're doing what you are supposed to be doing. The rest is up to Hashem. Just lift up your voice in prayer, wherever and whenever you can. Remember that you're doing what Hashem wants of you. There is no greater position in life than that."

❈ ❈ ❈

Esther and Bracha exchanged happy glances. Tomorrow's workload didn't seem quite so overwhelming anymore.

◢§ Twins and Triplets

When you hear the word *twins*, what do you imagine? Two sweet babies dressed in identical clothing, lying happily in their carriages, or two five year olds walking hand in hand on the sidewalk, or two mischievous students fooling their new teacher on the first day of school? Mothers of twins know there is more to twins than their identical appearance. And what applies to twins applies to triplets in triplicate. The manner in which you handle your twins or triplets will depend on their gender and the number of children in the family. Are they the firstborn? Or are there two other children, the oldest six years old? Were they born after a long break? Are they both girls, boys or one of each?

One of the challenges that twins and triplets present is simply the physical care they require when they are infants. It is well known they won't wait patiently to be taken care of. One infant crying to be fed, burped, changed, bathed, dressed, held and put down to sleep is usually sufficient enough to occupy a mother's time and energy. Managing twins demands much more prioritization, organization and help and managing triplets demands even more. With twins a mother feels that, if need be, she can physically hold both of her babies. But triplets require an extra hand or an extra mother! A mother feels she hasn't got a chance. So spiritual *chizuk* is very important and extra help is crucial.

There is a very special rebbetzin in Jerusalem, who, after raising her own triplets, made it her *mitzvah* to visit women who have given birth to triplets. She helps them get organized and gives them encouragement. Explaining that their current situation is difficult and every day is a struggle, she is quick to add that the future is bright. She always advises women to look to the future to gain perspective. When the young mother sees the face of this serene, content rebbetzin and listens to her soothing voice, she feels uplifted and more capable of facing the challenges ahead of her. To these young mothers, this rebbetzin is living proof that one can survive to enjoy the *nachas* of triplets.

Below are some of the coping mechanisms employed by the experts — mothers of twins and triplets.

Many mothers prefer to have their twins and triplets wake up and be fed at the same time. This type of schedule allows them to sleep or take care of their husbands and other children during the breaks. Other women prefer to wake them separately, so that each one can share special time with his mother.

Your scheduling decision may be affected by your choice of feeding method. Some women nurse both babies, some nurse one and bottle feed the other, some alternate, giving a bottle and nursing. This choice might also depend on the size of each baby and how well he eats. For triplets, try putting the baby who has just been fed into an infant seat to burp him. Using infant seats to bottle feed the others is also worth trying.

In addition, a decision must be made as to what sort of help a woman needs most and how it can be put to the best possible use. Remember that assistance comes in many forms: paper plates, convenience foods, an older daughter to feed the babies and take them out for an hour, a cleaning lady, a laundry service, a full-time, live-in nurse, an afternoon baby sitter, a night nurse or a cook.

Your decision will depend on the number of children you have and your financial situation. If, for example, you have school age children who need you in the afternoon, you may decide to hire an afternoon baby sitter or put the twins to sleep in the afternoons. If your children are older, they can help you care for the twins when they get home from school. Alternatively, let your sixth grader help your first grader with her homework while you attend to the infants. Many mothers of twins lower their standards of household maintenance and do only the minimum required to keep the house afloat. They cook simple meals or buy ready-made food and baked goods, use paper plates and the like. If finances permit, they hire a cleaning lady. The important thing at this stage (in addition to reminding yourself that "this too shall pass") is to carefully consider your options and then do whatever your situation allows for. Try to get as much rest as possible and remain calm and collected.

Make sure your household help (including family members) knows where the baby clothing is located, which outfit belongs to whom, what care the babies need and how they are to be fed. It is a good idea to label the babies' cribs, bottles, pacifiers and clothing. To prevent thrush and other contagious diseases from spreading from one baby to the other, color code their bottles and pacifiers. Put together a feeding chart to indicate who was fed, when and how much. Once you've made it to the point where each baby can be spoon-fed, it is worth your while to prepare enough food to feed them both at the same time. If possible, keep all necessary items in one room so you won't have to run from room to room to look for something you need. Consider preparing formula in advance, just washing the bottle after feeds.

As your twins become toddlers they will enjoy playing with each other and having each other as company. But beware, twins and triplets seem to get into double/triple trouble and mischief, as they can help each other and plan together. That's why some mothers prefer to put their twins in separate playpens. Sibling rivalry, fighting over toys, and competing for mother's attention starts at this time. One mother I know set aside one room, which she childproofed and filled with toys. Then her triplets could play in safety while she accomplished her chores. A door resembling the side of a playpen enabled her to see them while she worked and they, in turn didn't feel locked in. (This can be done with a gate used for stairs as well.)

Another difficulty concerns whether to buy double: two cribs, two high chairs, two walkers, two playpens, two infants seats, two. . . Not only is this inconvenient and space gobbling, but it may not even be financially feasible.

Two cribs and a double stroller, however, may be necessary. Two infant seats for feeding and burping are also handy. Some car seats can double as infant seats. If you drive, two car seats are essential. But one baby carriage might be able to accommodate two small infants and will cost less than a twin carriage. Often, these are so large and cumbersome that you'd rather not use them.

Just remember that if you lack the space, don't double up on items you might not need. When you go on an outing, you can put one baby in a carriage and one in a baby carrier. If you're at home doing chores, you can settle one baby in an infant seat and one in a playpen or swing. As they get older, seat one in the walker and let one crawl around on the floor. If you really feel you could use a particular item in duplicate, perhaps you could borrow it for the short amount of time that the baby needs it. Perhaps there is a *gemach* in your area to borrow from. Look for women who have older twins; they might have a double stroller in good condition which they might loan or sell to you.

As with all children, the older twins become, the easier it is to manage their physical care and the more their psychological and emotional needs come to the forefront. The biggest challenge at this stage is to view your twins as individuals and help them develop their own unique talents. This will be easier if one is a boy and the other a girl. If they are of the same gender you may want to consider sending them to different schools, or placing them in separate classes in the same school. If neither of these options are possible, you may want to make extra efforts to be in contact with the school staff *and* with your twins. To illustrate the importance of staying in touch in this way, one mother of twins told me that when one twin would say, "The teacher said. . .," the other would counter with, "Oh no she didn't," and a fight would invariably ensue. It quickly became clear to the mother that she had to be on top of the situation and so from then on she spoke with the teacher on a regular basis. After instituting this policy the children stopped arguing. Another mother reported that her twins became very dependent on one another, taking turns doing homework, so that one did the homework one night while the other copied, and vice versa the next night. Because of this, she separated them into two different classes.

Your twins might not have the same outside interests or talents or friends. So sign them up for different extracurricular activities. Many mothers find that sibling rivalry is reduced and the twins appreciate each other more when they're not together in school.

Above all, remember that twins and triplets are a unique challenge and a unique *brachah.* When a friend of mine with a house full of small children gave birth to twins, many people were concerned for her physical and emotional welfare. When I visited her she confided in me and said, "I don't understand everyone's attitude. I'm busy all day long with my children and I love it. I'm constantly doing *mitzvos.* I'm emulating Hashem. This is how I felt without the twins. Now I feel doubly blessed."

◂§ Afterward

So now you've read a book on household organization. What happens next? Maybe you're inspired and determined to organize your house once and for all. But the baby needs his shots and your daughter needs special tutoring . . . and your motivation seems to have been left on the shelf with this book.

You wonder if an organized home will really make such a difference. After all, you're used to things as they are. But be forewarned, once you take that first step towards organization, it will change your whole way of thinking. Little by little your daily life will become easier. Room by room your house will become organized. You'll find you have more storage options in your house than you ever thought possible. Not only will you be able to find things but so will the rest of your family. This will inspire you to remain organized and generate organized patterns and habits. You'll spend less time, not more, involved in household management and the time you spend will be more enjoyable.

Appendix A — Meal Lists

List of the foods your family enjoys.
It is a useful tool for menu planning.

Milchig and Pareve Meals

1. French Toast
2. Fried matzah (matzah brei)
3. Spaghetti or noodles
   w/ketchup
   w/tomato sauce
   w/cheese sauce
   w/tomato and cheese sauce
   w/sour cream, sugar and
      cinnamon
   w/vegetables
4. Spicy Noodle Casserole
   w/mushrooms
   w/squash or other vegetable
   sweet w/ raisins
5. Toasted cheese:
   open-faced
   closed
   in pita w/ tomato sauce
      or ketchup
6. Rice
   and steamed vegetables
      (w/techinah)
   casserole — spicy or sweet
      w/sugar and cinnamon
7. Eggs
   omelet (w/cheese)
   pizza omelet
   scrambled (w/cheese)
   sunny-side-up
   Rocky Mountain toast
   baked w/flour and vegetables
      (and cheese)
8. Eggplant Parmesan
   w/noodles
   w/rice

9. Borekas
   vegetable
   cheese
   potato
10. Blintzes
    cheese
    potato
    fruit or jelly
11. Cheese pancakes
12. Quiche
13. Felafel
14. Soup
    (see special section below)
15. Potatoes:
    mashed w/sour cream
    baked w/sour cream
    w/melted cheese
    w/tuna
    sliced
    French fries
    kugel
    latkes
    potato salad

Fleishig Main Dishes

1. Meat burgers
2. Chicken burgers
3. Schnitzel
4. Chicken
   roasted w/spices
   fried
   mustard and ketchup
   mustard and honey
   w/barbeque sauce
   w/duck sauce (i.e. apricot jam)
   stuffed and sliced

w/vinegar and garlic
w/mushroom sauce
batter fried
batter baked
broiled
in orange sauce
curried
5. Hot dogs
6. Cold cuts
7. Meatballs w/spaghetti or rice
8. Stuffed cabbage
9. Stuffed peppers
10. Pepper beef w/rice
11. Chinese meat w/vegetables
12. Roast   •
13. Kugel w/meat
14. Shepherd's pie

Side Dishes

Potatoes
    (see milchig and parve main
    dishes)
Rice
Kishke
Blintzes w/vegetables
Borekas
Knishes
Kugel
    carrot
    squash
    potato
    bread
Steamed Vegetables

Appetizers

Borekas
    vegetable
    potato and meat
    meat and vegetable
    hot dog
    liver

Chopped liver on lettuce or toast
Mock chopped liver
Meatballs w/ rice or noodles
Curry and rice
Stuffed Pepper
Egg Salad
Stuffed Avocado
Chicken Salad
Fish
Salads

Fish

Gefilte
Broiled (Marinated in oil, lemon
   and spices)
Baked
    w/techinah
    w/sour cream
    w/vegetables
    w/tomato sauce or ketchup
    w/mayonnaise and ketchup
    w/Italian dressing
Fried in sweet and sour sauce
Cooked in pan w/ curry
Tuna
    salad
    noodle casserole
    patties
Fish Salad
    w/ eggs
    w/ noodles

Salads

Tomato
Squash
Corn
    pickles, pepper, celery and
      mayonnaise
    cooked squash, fried onion
    pineapple, celery and
      mayonnaise

Cucumber, radish, pickle, carrot
  w/ lemon juice or vinegar,
    and sugar
Kohlrabi
  w/ carrots, cucumber, oil,
    vinegar
  w/ carrots and mayonnaise
Beet
  w/ orange juice
  w/ cumin and lemon
  w/ vinegar
  w/ pickles, potatoes and
    vinegar
Greenbean w/ vinaigrette marinade
Spinach or lettuce
  w/ peas, mushrooms, hard-
    boiled egg, mayonnaise
    and mustard dressing
Potato
  w/ mustard, vinegar,
    mayonnaise
  w/ eggs, onion, celery,
    green pepper, pickle,
    mayonnaise and mustard
  w/ mayonnaise, carrots,
    peas, pickles
Coleslaw
  w/ mayonnaise
  w/ cucumber, carrot, vinegar,
    sugar, oil and pepper
Squash
  sautéed w/ tumeric and onion,
    served hot or cold
  cooked w/ tomato sauce,
    onions, wine and garlic
    served hot or cold
Radish w/ carrot, pickles,
  green pepper, and lemon
Carrots
  grated w/ mayonnaise
  grated w/ orange juice

grated w/ lemon, dates, raisins
cooked w/ oil, lemon, paprika
Noodle
  w/ mayonnaise, celery
    and onion
  w/ mayonnaise, celery,
    and chicken

Soups
Note the following abbreviations:
  d = dairy, m = meat, p = parve
Chicken
Onion (d or m)
Leek Potato (p or d)
Potato (p or d)
Cucumber (d)
Greenbean (d)
Vegetable (d, m or p)
Tomato (d or m)
Borsht (d)
Cabbage (p or d)
Corn (m or d)
Sweet and sour (m)

Food List for Special Diet
1. Fish and
   beets
   corn
   stir-fried vegetables
   baked butternut or acorn squash
2. Millet and peanut butter
3. Oatmeal and soy sauce
4. Whole wheat farina
5. Cornmeal and lentils with chili
6. Whole wheat noodles
   w/ tomato sauce
7. Vegetable sautée
   w/rice and techinah sauce
8. Vegetable combinations:
   stir-fried carrots with cabbage
     and celery

carrots, zucchini, potatoes,
onion, tomato sauce
and bay leaf
9. Baked potatoes
w/ techinah and salad
10. Whole wheat sandwiches:
almond butter
peanut butter
avocado
techinah
11. Soups:
tomato rice soup

cabbage
minestrone
pea
vegetable soup
vegetable soup thickened with
oatmeal, millet or cornmeal
sweet potato
12. Vegetarian chili
13. Soy patties
14. Soy in tomato sauce
w/ noodles or rice

Appendix B: Weekly Menu Plans

The following is a two-week menu plan using the "cook-once-a-week" system. A majority of the cooking is done on Thursday and will provide for Thursday's dinner, all Shabbos meals, Sunday's dinner and even Monday's dinner.

Sample Menu A			
Shabbos meals	**appetizer**	**main dish**	**dessert**
Friday Night	Cold Fruit soup	Orange chicken w/Rice Cauliflower	Chocolate mousse
Shabbos Day	Chicken salad	Potato kugel and Schnitzel and Salad	Chocolate mousse
Third Meal	Fried fish w/sweet and sour sauce Noodle vegetable casserole Cucumber salad w/lemon Cold squash salad		

meal	Sunday	Monday	Tuesday	Wednesday	Thursday
lunch	Chicken Soup	Baked Potatoes w/ Salad	French Toast	Fried Eggs w/ Tomato and Toast	Noodles w/ Cheese
dinner	Shabbos Leftovers	Veg. Soup Fried Fish & Potatoes	Chicken and Potato salad	Noodles w/ Cheese Lettuce Salad	Baked, Sliced Potatoes w/ Cuc. Sal. Chicken or Fish

Sample Menu B			
Shabbos meals	**appetizer**	**main dish**	**dessert**
Friday Night	Chicken soup w/ Noodles	B-B-Q chicken & Potatoes Green Beans	Chocolate cake
Shabbos Day	*Borekas* w/ Lettuce Salad	Cholent Cold Chicken Fried Shnitzel	Chocolate cake
Third Meal	Tuna Salad, Egg Salad, Cuc. Salad w/ Sour Cream Carrot Salad w/ Lemon, Quiche		

meal	Sunday	Monday	Tuesday	Wednesday	Thursday
lunch	Chicken Soup w/ Noodles & Salad	Noodles w/ Cheese	Omelet w/ Salad	Fried Matzah Tomato	Toasted Cheese Pickles & Tomatoes
dinner	Shabbos Leftovers	Quiche Cuc. Salad	Fish, Rice Vegetables	Noodle-Veg. Casserole w/ Cheese	Fish Potato Kugel Squash Sal.

MENU PLAN FOR "COOK-DOUBLE" SYSTEM

Sample Menu C					
	Sunday	**Monday**	**Tuesday**	**Wednesday**	**Thursday**
cook-double system	Pancakes (make extra batter)	Veg.-Noodle Casserole (make extra noodles for macaroni & cheese)	Fish & Potatoes Vegetables (use extra vegetables for soup)	Soup and Macaroni & Cheese	Make 2 Quiches and freeze one

meal	Sunday	Monday	Tuesday	Wednesday	Thursday
lunch	Pancakes & Fruits	Cheese Sandwich w/ Tomato	Pancakes w/ Salad	Veg.-Noodle Casserole	Quiche and Salad
dinner	Shabbos Leftovers	Veg.-Noodle Casserole w/ Salad	Fish & Potatoes Vegetables	Quiche and Salad	Chicken Pie

REGULAR WEEKLY MENU
Sample Menu D

This menu is easy to remember but still gives some choice.
It's great for people who like knowing that if it's Monday it must be meatloaf.

meal	Sunday	Monday	Tuesday	Wednesday	Thursday
dinner	Shabbos Leftovers	Meatloaf & Potatoes; or Burgers and Fries; or Spaghetti & Meatballs; or Chili Green salad	Fish w/ Rice or Potatoes w/ Cooked Vegetables; or Tuna-Noodle Casserole	Quiche and Macaroni & Cheese; Vegetarian Chili; Pizza; Vegetable Casserole w/ Salad	Meat or Chicken Potato w/ Salad Vegetables
For Shabbos meals — see menu plan A and B					

VEGETARIAN DIETS
Sample Menu E

Meal plan for vegetarian diets with no milk products
(no fruit and vegetable combination or starch and protein combination).

Sunday	Monday	Tuesday	Wednesday	Thursday	Friday Night
Baked Potato w/ Techinah or Clarified Butter Salad	Vegetable Soup Millet w/Soy Sauce or Peanut But.	Vegetable Casserole w/ Lentils or Soy	Fish w/ Mixed Vegetables	Sweet Potato Soup and Peppers Stuffed with Rice	Lentil Soup Tofu or Fish Stir-Fry Vegetables Rice
Shabbos Lunch		Vegetable Combo w/ Tofu; Vegetarian Chili; Salad			
Shabbos — Third Meal		Fish; Salad			

Appendix C — Freezer Hints

HOW TO DEFROST:

■ **Precooked vegetables** — don't need thawing; cook in a small amount of boiling salt water.

■ **Meat and chicken** — Defrost overnight in fridge. Fast thawing destroys taste.

■ **Bakery goods** — Unwrap and thaw.

■ **Sauces** — May be heated while frozen in a double boiler.

Use thawed food as soon as possible. Freezing prevents the normal bacterial growth process, but once defrosted the process is speeded up.

ITEMS WHICH FREEZE WELL AND ARE PRACTICAL TO FREEZE:

hot soups (w/o potatoes)	kugel (most types)
quiche	*borekas*
blintzes	kreplach
chicken	schnitzel
fried fish	cooked eggplant
squash	shlishkas
meatballs	stuffed cabbage
roast turkey	meat burgers
knishes	kishke
gefilte fish	stuffed cabbage
stuffed peppers	cakes
pies	

DON'T FREEZE:

milk products, hard-boiled eggs, bananas, mayonnaise, cooked potatoes, tomatoes, anything juicy like pears, melon, salad greens or cucumber.

Spices lose their zip when frozen. Bay leaves, basil, oregano, parsley, dill, may turn bitter. [Better to add these spices before serving.]

About the Authors

In 1986 Nechamah Berg and Chaya Levine founded Creative Options, a home management consulting service, which offers a wide range of solutions to household management problems and offers vocational counseling for female entrepreneurs.

They have lectured to hundreds of Jewish women on the topics of time management, meal management, and household organization.

They write a popular weekly newspaper column entitled "Tips for the Home."

5